"I Don't Know What You Want of Me."

"Think of us. Now. This minute," Julian said. "Forget everything and everyone else. Why can't you do that?"

"I'm a realist," Ann replied.

He raised his head and faced her. His fingers gripped her shoulders and she tried to wrench free, but he would not let her go.

"I'm tired of this foolishness. Tired of battling you all the time. It's time I taught you a lesson, Ann Milan. A lesson of love—"

His eyes were blazing as his lips crushed down on hers. . . .

TRACY ADAMS

has traveled extensively throughout all our fifty states. She prefers to use American settings for her novels as she is firmly convinced that America is truly the land of romance. When you read her books, we think you'll agree.

Dear Reader:

Silhouette Romances is an exciting new publishing venture. We will be presenting the very finest writers of contemporary romantic fiction as well as outstanding new talent in this field. It is our hope that our stories, our heroes and our heroines will give you, the reader, all you want from romantic fiction.

Also, *you* play an important part in our future plans for Silhouette Romances. We welcome any suggestions or comments on our books and I invite you to write to us at the address below.

So, enjoy this book and all the wonderful romances from Silhouette. They're for *you!*

Karen Solem
Editor-in-Chief
Silhouette Books
P.O. Box 769
New York, N.Y. 10019

TRACY ADAMS
The Moth and the Flame

Silhouette Romance

Published by Silhouette Books New York

America's Publisher of Contemporary Romance

SILHOUETTE BOOKS, a Simon & Schuster Division of
GULF & WESTERN CORPORATION
1230 Avenue of the Americas, New York, N.Y. 10020

ISBN: 0-671-57086-2

First Silhouette printing June, 1981

10 9 8 7 6 5 4 3 2 1

The Moth
and the Flame

Chapter One

The late afternoon meeting in the attorney's office was a disaster. Ann Milan sat with her hands clenched in her lap, listening, unbelieving, while her brother David was immobilized, a mixture of emotions on his face.

"I don't believe it!" Ann said. "I simply can't and won't believe that Dad has left us penniless."

"Sorry, Miss Milan, I'm afraid that's the picture. I wish it were otherwise. The debts are staggering. Your father had one run of bad luck after another, and it would seem that his judgment on investments had grown exceedingly worse in the past few months."

"The estate?" David asked fearfully.

"It will fall into the hands of your creditors. As well as anything there of value. All the paintings, sculpture, the furniture—"

"Perhaps you want our souls, too!" Ann spat out vehemently, leaping up to pace about.

The room grew silent, and David came to put a hand on her shoulder. "Calm down, sis. It's not the end of the world."

"It might as well be! Just how do you propose we live, David, without a red cent to our names? You only know how to play tennis, golf and appreciate the arts. I'm not much better. I've already sold most of my jewelry. We've been living on that the last few weeks. Now that's nearly gone, too!"

"You'll have to go to work. Both of you," the attorney said. "Don't look so horrified. Most people do, you know."

Despair had come to settle around Ann like an ominous cloud. She wanted to rage against the world, hit back, show them that this simply could not be happening to them. Dad had been a proud man. One of the best investment brokers in the business. How could it have come to this?

"You must vacate your house within a week, Ann," the attorney said. "We've stalled as long as we can. Sorry—"

Ever since their father had died of a massive coronary several months ago, they had feared this day. Even from the beginning they had been warned that, more than likely, their father's estate would come down to a final zero. Now with all reports in Ann knew that her pride had come to the same terrible finality. Zero!

"Let's get out of here, David," Ann said.

David rose up out of his chair. He had always

followed his older sister's lead. Now he hastened after her out of the attorney's office, matching her quick-paced steps as the hard heels of her knee-high patent leather boots struck the floor with sharp anger and equal frustration.

How could their world have come to this?

"Slow down, Ann," David said. "It's not going to do any good to react like this."

Her reply was to slam the door behind her with a motion that could easily have shattered the glass. She sped down the hall to the elevator, her last fur draped around her shoulders, her fashionably mid-calf length skirt swishing in her anger. Color heightened her cheekbones, her dark blue eyes were sparking with silver fire, and her full sensuous mouth had hardened ever so little.

"Don't pretend you're not as shattered as I!" she said with clenched teeth. "From the golden boy of Darshire to this!"

He lifted a brow. "It's a heck of a note, isn't it? Who would have thought that you and I—?"

Ann's pride and emotions took a sudden nosedive, and her eyes misted with tears. She tried to flick them away, but it was no use. They trickled down her cheeks.

She had managed to keep her car, a low slung foreign affair that would do eighty without even trying. To have taken the car away from her would have been the final straw.

"Look, you like adventure," David said. "This might even be kind of fun, going out and rubbing elbows with all those working people—"

"It's the humiliation of it. We'll be the scandal of Darshire," Ann said.

She shot him a glance that was meant to wilt him and usually did. But this time he only gave her a crooked smile. "We're both college educated. We can manage, and we will, sis."

"Sure," she sighed. "Oh, sure!"

Twilight was falling on the raw January day. Piles of dirty snow lined the freeway, and the wind still had a bite that even penetrated the fur around her neck.

She took the wheel and with a lurch sent the car out into the line of traffic. David gave her a scowl. "You trying to kill us or something?"

"I want to get home and find some way to cope with all of this."

"You will. I will. Listen, we'll work it out."

"How?" she asked bitterly.

"Marry one of your handsome men. You have plenty of them always coming around," David said. "It's easy for a woman. Now a man has to look hard to find a rich girl to marry—"

"Oh, be quiet, David! Just be quiet, will you?"

She pressed the accelerator pedal down hard, and the mighty engine throbbed with power as they shot down the freeway, passing everything in front of them.

At their exit Ann slowed the car.

"You took that curve on two wheels," David protested. "Now cool off, Ann!"

She eased up slightly, and soon they had left Darshire behind. Their country estate was a few miles out of the city, an elaborate showplace that their father had loved. To Ann and David it was home. It tore at Ann's heart to realize that it had been lost along with everything else.

Ann cut her speed as they neared the inn. It was a rambling rustic building, tucked away in the Vermont hills, held in the arms of the small valley where the trees put on a splendid array of color every autumn. It was an old establishment that had been going downhill in recent years—until Julian Terrace had arrived from New York and began putting new life into it. Now it was very successful.

Julian Terrace! Ann's lips made a straight, hard line at the thought of him. How stupid of her to think of him now, after all this time. Worst of all, it was shattering to realize she could have been so gullible. She knew how most men operated. How suave some of them could be, how most of them were out for a good time and not much else.

David glanced at the inn as well. "Wonder how soon that place will be open?"

"Couple of months, I suppose."

"I thought you sort of fell for Julian Terrace last fall," David said.

"Don't be ridiculous!" Ann snapped.

But David could read her like a book. Sometimes she forgot how perceptive he could be.

Julian! Her heart throbbed remembering him and that one sweet, short night when she had been held in his arms. It was the night of the Autumn Ball at the inn. She had gone there with friends, for it was the "in" place to go. She had seen Julian a few times, caught glimpses of him driving his sports car or swatting a tennis ball on the courts. Once she'd seen him in swimming trunks, diving from the high board, his sun bronzed body beautifully male and strong. Everytime she had seen him, she felt drawn to him. She had anticipated the ball because it would give her a chance to see him again.

The moment they walked inside, she sensed his presence. She spied him standing at the ballroom door, greeting each of his guests. No man had ever looked so perfect in evening clothes. The coat draped his shoulders in a casual but splendid way. The dark tie and ruffled shirt made him seem all the more virile. His trousers emphasized the long, lean length of him, and he stood solidly, feet apart, a man never to be taken lightly.

His hair was black and thick, falling into a deep wave, barely touching his coat collar. Heavy brows arched above dark eyes. His voice had a pleasant deep rumble as he spoke to his guests. Ann found her breath caught as she stepped nearer. He turned to greet her with a quick, purposeful motion as if he, too, had sensed her presence. His dark gaze swept over her, appraising with obvious pleasure. His brows drew together as he reached out his hand and closed his fingers around hers.

"Hello," he murmured.

She felt scorched, burned by his touch. Never in her life had she found it difficult to come up with a tart or saucy answer, but tonight her voice failed her.

"Ann Milan, I believe," he said.

She was startled that he knew her name, but pleased that he must have been interested enough to ask someone.

"Yes. Good evening, Mr. Terrace?"

He nodded slightly, amused. "Oh, *you* may call me Julian."

His mouth was full, sensuous. His face was bony with a look of lean hunger. He was clearly a man she would never forget.

His hand finally dropped away, but his gaze held her. She felt captured, imprisoned.

"Save me a dance, will you?"

Before she could answer, he had turned to the next guest and the moment was gone.

Pretending to join in with the laughter and conversation of her friends, she watched closely for another glimpse of him. With a delicious tingle she often found him staring at her, even from across the room.

She was conscious of waiting nervously, afraid he would forget, that someone else would claim his time. Then, at last, he came to her, walking with his long stride. He reached out his hands to her.

"Our dance."

It was more of a command than an invitation.

She moved into his arms, mesmerized by his dark eyes. The moment he pulled her close, she felt the excitement begin to pound in her heart.

They talked about the inn, her friends, the ball, which he hoped to turn into an annual affair, and all the while he seemed to hold her closer. His lips brushed her hair in an enticing way. She loved the feel of his strong shoulders beneath her hand, the warmth of his arms around her. It was hard not to tremble.

"Let's get some air," he said, and there was hidden fire in his eyes. Bright threads of excitement began to weave through her heart.

It was not like her to lose her head like this, but with every passing moment she knew she was falling more and more under his spell.

The scent of autumn leaves rushed out to them as they stepped away from the inn. The sky was incredibly clear, punctured by silver stars. The music drifted out on the night air, and as they walked, his arm slid possessively around her waist. Acutely aware of his tall, masculine body, her throat swelled shut. No man had effected her like this before. No man ever would again.

When they reached the lake, the water lapping at the shore, she felt the night surround them as if to pull them closer together.

"All the while we danced, I was thinking of this moment," he murmured. "I was hoping you'd come tonight."

"I didn't know you even knew my name!"

He stroked her cheek with his fingertips, and a blaze of electricity jolted along her nerves.

"Oh, I know you," he murmured. "I've seen you around, and I've wanted to speak with you—"

Her heart was beating with a rapid pounding. His fingers twisted suddenly into her hair, and she trembled beneath his caress.

"Ann, come here!" he said.

It was a brusque, urgent request. With a swift

motion he pulled her into his arms. His mouth came down with a fiery kiss. Its intensity grew as he molded his lean body against hers. She was shot full of a strange, wondrous desire, and a soft moan escaped her lips.

"I knew it would be like this," he breathed. "You set my blood on fire, Ann!"

He kissed her over and over again, and she found herself clinging to him as she had never clung to any other man.

"I must see you again," he said.

She was caught up in the whirlwind of his passion.

"Tomorrow?"

He laughed with delight. "Of course. Come to the inn, and I'll buy you lunch. Perhaps we can go for a drive or have a game of tennis—whatever you like, Ann. So long as I see you—"

He bent his head to cover her mouth with still one more ardent kiss when they were disturbed by the sound of footsteps. There was a polite cough.

"Excuse me, Mr. Terrace."

Julian was annoyed. "What is it?"

"There is someone at the front desk to see you."

"I'll be along later."

"It's—it's Miss Irene, sir."

Julian swore under his breath. He tensed up, and with stiff shoulders and a hard set to his jaw he turned away from Ann.

"All right. I'll be there in a moment," he said with an air of resignation.

The desk clerk scurried away. Julian stood very quietly, fists knotted.

She wondered who Irene was. Perhaps an important guest.

"I'm sorry, Ann. Walk back with me? The moment I'm free, I'll come back to find you—"

She tried to match his long, hurried strides, his arm pulling her snugly beneath his shoulder where she seemed to fit perfectly. When they reached the lights of the ballroom, he seemed distant and moody.

"Later, Ann—"

Then he was gone, and with a feeling of overpowering loss she sighed and went back to find her friends who were the noisiest in the place. They always knew how to have a good time. She tried to join in, waiting impatiently for Julian to come back. There was no sign of him. Restlessly she searched the room for him and was about to go to the front desk and ask for him when her friends decided to leave.

"I'm not ready to go," she argued. "Why must we go just when everyone is having such a good time?"

But she was overruled and swept away under protest. With an air of regret she left the inn. But she would come back tomorrow. She would see him again!

It was nearly noon the next day when she drove to the inn and hurried across the lobby to the desk.

"Where can I find Mr. Terrace?" she asked.

The clerk behind the desk shook his head.

"He's out. He'll be away for some time."

"I don't understand. We had—well, we were going to have lunch together—"

The clerk was inclined to gossip and leaned toward her with a smirking grin on his face.

"His wife showed up here last night, fit to be tied. She started to make a scene, and he hustled her away to his private apartment. Then the first thing this morning they left for Europe."

"Wife!" she gasped. "Europe!"

The clerk seemed to be enjoying her bewilderment.

"I hear he intends to buy her a villa on the French Riviera. She's part of the jet set, you know. Always making demands on Julian, and the poor fool always knuckles under to her—"

Ann was sickened by this shattering news. She rushed out to her car and drove off, head reeling. A wife! He was married. How dare he lure her out to the shadows and kiss her like that? How dare he lead her to believe that he cared for her and ask to see her again?

What a fool I've been, she told herself. *Imagine, Ann Milan, being taken in by a rogue like that!*

She went back into her busy whirl of things, putting him out of her mind the best she could.

A couple of weeks later, she came in to find a message. Julian had phoned and requested that she return his call.

With an angry gesture she tore the message into bits. She had her rules, and one of them was *never* to become involved with a married man!

She didn't visit the inn again, and Julian didn't phone. Then suddenly everything began to fall apart. Her father was dead, and everything was in a horrible mess. Her world had been so good. Now it was shattered. Remembering the disastrous meeting she and David had just attended, she was brought back to reality.

She began to drive fast again, her emotions churning. She and David were all but penniless! Neither was equipped to handle a disaster like this.

"Look out!" David shouted.

She didn't see the other car. It was as simple as that. When she did, it was too late. She spun the wheel to swerve out of the way, but not in time. Suddenly the car was out of control, heading for the median between the traffic lanes. Then it was bouncing up and over, steel crunching, horn blowing, lights flashing everywhere. She heard David calling again, then there was only the oblivion of darkness. . . .

Four months had passed since the accident. Though Ann's own cuts and bruises had healed quickly, it had been another story for David. She had spent many long hours at the hospital wondering if David would ever walk again. Finally, she heard that he would be immobilized for some time to come. Not forever, the doctor assured her, but the recovery would be slow and painful . . . a wheelchair for months, then crutches, then a cane, and at last, if he behaved himself, he would be his old, active self.

Ann despaired. She hated to see her brother suffer and bitterly blamed herself for the accident. She grieved for her father and the golden world that had been shattered. They were now practically broke and David was in no position to do anything about it. In the best of times they had been improvident . . . and now?

Well, she was a Milan, and she could do it. She enrolled in a secretarial school and took up accounting. She spent days looking for a small, suitable place that she and David could share. She sold her car—the damage had been minimal—to pay for much needed medical attention for David. She found an outlet for her furs and sold the last of her jewelry, her mother's diamond pin and her gold bracelet. Her wardrobe now consisted of a few remaining good pieces, accented by carefully chosen cheaper things that she made look expensive with her taste and flair for clothes.

Her humiliation had turned to quiet resignation. Never had she been what she thought was a true beauty, her face now held more character through the knowledge of pain and despair. A little line creased its way above her nose. Her eyes no longer flashed with quick temper. She was in control of herself more than she had ever been. Not by choice but necessity.

One day, not long ago, David had dropped a bombshell.

"I have news. I heard Julian was divorced several months ago."

"Divorced?" she asked, trying not to show interest.

"I understand his ex-wife is a hell cat. Demanding and difficult. Throws jealous tantrums."

"I really don't care, David," she snapped.

He ignored that, knowing better.

"He's been generous. He's bought her a fancy villa on the French Riviera and supplies her with money for which she apparently hounds him all the time."

"Is that so?" Ann said coolly. "And does he jet over to see her?"

David licked his lips and shrugged. "That's just speculation. I'm not sure anyone knows for certain. Only that he goes to Europe occasionally—"

What kind of man is he, hanging around his ex-wife all the time? she wondered bitterly. *Obviously, he's the sort who takes whatever he wants when he wants it!*

She tried to poison her mind with such ideas, and most of the time it worked. There was no place for Julian Terrace in her shattered world, even if he proved to be a saint instead of a devil.

The most pressing thing right now was to find employment. Inexperienced as she was, she quickly learned it wasn't easy. Then David showed her an ad in the newspaper.

"Julian Terrace needs help at the inn," he said, giving her a long, thoughtful look.

"I wouldn't work for a man like that if our lives depended on it!"

David drew a deep breath, "I wish I could help. I wish I could *do* something—"

Ann put a quick hand on her brother's shoulder. "You will be able to soon, David. It's just a question of time. In the meanwhile, I guess I should consider the job. It probably pays well and it is close by. . . . What the heck? Of course I'll apply. What can we lose?"

"Are you sure—?"

She put a smile on her face for her brother's benefit.

"Of course."

Now she sat outside Julian's office, heart pounding, hands twisted together, wondering at her bold words. Every nerve was honed to a razor's edge. He kept her waiting and waiting.

"Miss Milan."

She jumped at the sound of his voice. He stood in the doorway, appraising her with his dark, cold eyes. He was instantly defensive and arrogant. He wore dark trousers and a pale blue shirt open at the neck, revealing a strong throat suntanned, no doubt, from visits to his ex-wife!

"Sorry to keep you waiting. I'm free now. Please, come in."

He moved away with long, impatient strides. She followed him and took the chair he motioned to her. He stood at his desk with authority, like a man at the wheel of his ship. His sardonic scowl raked her up and down.

"So, you've come to apply for work."

She hated to crawl to this man who obviously thought he was God's gift to women! Yet she was still all too aware of him, of the slope of his hard jaw, the glitter of his eyes, the breadth of those shoulders she had so lovingly caressed that night under the stars. It seemed so long ago now.

"I feel I'm qualified," she said evenly.

"I'm not the easiest man to work for. My last two secretaries didn't last long."

She lifted her chin. "From the looks of that mess on your desk, you need someone rather badly."

He favored her with a cool smile.

"If I hire you for this job, you may be required to handle the hostess job for a couple of nights a week relieving Mrs. Stevenson."

She flushed. Many of her old friends still came here. It wouldn't be easy to suddenly be put in a position of servitude. Her pride was stung at the thought.

"I'll do whatever is required," she said stiffly.

He came around the desk toward her. Her pulse leaped as he moved past her. For a moment he was so near she could have touched him.

He opened the door to the outer office and motioned to the accumulation of papers on the secretary's desk there.

"I'd like you to start in the morning," he said. "Even this afternoon, if possible."

She was so stunned that for a moment she couldn't believe her ears.

"It's a seasonal job, as you know," he continued. "Last of October the inn closes, and I'll have no further need of you."

"I understand. And if you like, I'll start now."

He shrugged and nodded. "I never like wasting time."

"I'm aware of *that!*" she said drily.

His gaze devoured her for half a second, and then

22

he turned away as if she were not a person at all but a piece of furniture.

"I'd like to make a phone call first," Ann said.

He shrugged. "Use that one out there. Then come back in here, and I'll dictate some letters. On the double. I want to clear this mess off my desk today, if possible."

Even as she stepped out of the room, she wasn't certain she'd done it. She found the phone and reached for it.

David took awhile to answer, but was elated to hear she'd gotten the job.

"If you need anything, ring me here, David, or call Mrs. Clauson from next door."

"I'll be okay!" he insisted. "Congratulations, Ann!"

She said goodbye, snatched up a steno pad, and rushed back into Julian's office. He was just coming out, and they collided in the doorway. With a flush she was acutely aware of his tall, hard body, and the contact, though brief, sent her senses reeling.

"It seems I recall another time when you and I stood close like this," he said with a glitter in his dark eyes. "The Autumn Ball—the stars—"

She wrenched free of his hands as he steadied her. In a moment she might weaken and drown in his dark eyes.

"You don't return phone calls either," he said.

She lifted her chin. "My father died about that time. I haven't been socializing. Now I believe you said you had some dictation," she replied in a cold tone.

She would never, never, never let him know that she remembered the ball or cared that he had phoned. She marched into the office, and in a moment he followed. He stormed to his desk with angry steps. He began issuing orders faster than she could digest them.

"Just take this jumble of papers and put them in some kind of order. I have some phone calls to make. I don't want to see anyone or be bothered with silly questions. Understand?"

She did what he asked, glad that in the past few months she had learned a great deal by handling the tangle of her father's affairs.

The offices for the inn were located away from the main lobby, tucked into the south wing. The grounds surrounding the inn were well kept with gardens, trees and a small lake. It had once been rather quaint, with a touch of old fashioned charm. Now that was changing, for everywhere she could see Julian's suave sophistication. In the main dining room, the coffee shop and the bar, Julian had put his deft touch to arrangements and decoration. The second and third stories were taken up with guest rooms and suites.

Julian's door ripped open, and he came storming out, a look of black anger on his face.

"Some people do their damnedest to spoil a man's day," he said. "Do you know what the world is coming to? Incompetent idiots, that's what!"

He pulled open a file drawer and plucked out a thick folder.

An hour later she was still sorting through the papers he'd given her when he came out again.

"Lunch time," he said, striding away.

He certainly was interested in how she was getting along! She labored straight through the lunch hour—hearing people out in the lobby as they came and went. It sounded like a busy day. When Julian returned, he stopped at her desk, scowling.

"Really, Miss Milan, it's not necessary to starve just to make a good impression on your first day."

She picked up a pile of statements from the desk.

"These are *far* past due, did you realize that? Some of the follow-up letters about them haven't been exactly polite or pleasant."

He snatched them from her hand, his fingers brushing hers with a tingle of electricity. He swore under his breath. "I thought these had been paid some time ago! I think if you'll look, you'll find—"

"I already checked the ledger. They're not paid."

He stared at her and shook his head. "Blast!"

He went into his office, kicking the door shut behind him. Ann decided it was time for a lunch break, and if she ran into old acquaintances—well, there had to be a first time. She might as well spice up their otherwise dull luncheon conversation. She and David were on everyone's tongues these days. Worst of all, she knew what they were saying.

Wild things. Like she had tried to kill them both in the accident. Stupid things. Such as her father had been involved with a criminal syndicate based in New York. Idiotic things, he had a woman on the side who had cleaned out his pockets, and that was why he was in such terrible financial straits when he died. Really infuriating things, he had been nothing but a fast-talking charmer who had wrongly advised people in their investments and had taken kick-backs from certain companies. Dad had been many things, but he had never been dishonest. Ann knew that with all her heart, and no one would ever change her mind about it.

She was relieved that no one paid the slightest bit of attention to her in the dining room. Halfway through a chefs salad, Julian appeared. She heard his swift step, and her nerves froze.

"Where have you hidden the checkbook?" he asked.

His eyes were flashing dangerously as he glowered at her.

"How can I pay these bills?" he demanded.

"The checkbook is on your desk. I gave it to you along with the statements—"

"Miss Milan, I demand efficiency from my employees. I am not a tolerant man, and time wasted is a crime, and *you're* wasting my time—"

She flung down her napkin and got to her feet. "I think this whole idea of being your secretary is a horrible mistake—"

She walked out of the room, so furious she could barely see straight. All she wanted was to run away, to go home to David, to close the door to her miserably shabby bedroom and cry her eyes out.

Julian was coming behind her, his steps overtaking her. He caught her by the arm, his fingers cold and hard against her flesh.

"Sorry. I didn't mean to sound so rude and impatient."

She wrenched free of him. Without a word she went on ahead of him, marched into his office, and within a few seconds uncovered his checkbook from beneath a stack of papers.

He gave her a lifted brow and a trace of a smile. "I must have overlooked it."

"I'll be going now. Find yourself another secretary, Mr. Terrace."

"Cool off, will you? I said I was sorry. What more do you want?"

She gave him a quick look. "Respect. I'm really in no mood for your boorishness."

He tossed the checkbook down to his desk again and lifted his wide shoulders. "If I say I'm sorry again, will it help?"

He smiled then, and all defenses shattered.

"All right," she sighed.

"Good. Now let's both concentrate on clearing our desks."

He kept her after hours. Without apology, merely demanding her time as if she had no other life outside the inn. She let it pass. The extra pay in her envelope would be welcome.

When she was able to go at last, he was behind closed doors on the telephone. Bone weary, nerves still taut from the ups and down of the day, she drove away from the inn. Her little foreign car had been sold but she still had the Volkswagen van. It was functional, especially for David. These days, all considerations had to be for him.

The inn was a few miles out of Darshire, and it took ten minutes for her to drive home. Home! The word twisted in her heart. Their estate had consisted of nearly a hundred acres of ground, landscaped to the hilt, on a hill overlooking the rolling Vermont countryside. Now it was up for grabs. No one had bought it from the hands of the receivers. Because they were greedy. They wanted far too much money for it.

The house in town she had taken for David and herself was small, but the rooms were arranged so that they were convenient for David. It was old, needed paint inside and out, but the rent was reasonable. It was affordable. Perhaps someday they could move to something better. It had been suggested at the onset of her father's troubles that they simply move out of the neighborhood, even the state. That had stuck in Ann's pride like thorns.

"No. I won't turn tail and run," she had said. "This is our home. We'll stay."

And they had.

David met her at the door. He had grown thin since the accident, but he'd learned to handle the wheelchair expertly. Still it thrust knives of pain into Ann's heart whenever she saw him sitting in it, even though she knew it was only temporary.

"Hey, you pulled it off!" he laughed. "I knew you could. So you wowed Julian Terrace."

"Not exactly," she said, managing a laugh. "It's more that I caught him in a desperate moment. His office is in a mess."

She gave his shoulder an affectionate squeeze. At least one good thing had come from all of this. She and David had never been closer.

"We're all we have," he'd told her one day. "Each other. Let's stick."

"We're already stuck," she replied.

Now David was urging her to come and see what he'd done with his day. On a small table near the window he'd begun taking up an old hobby of wood carving. His figures were always those in motion, horses running, planes soaring off the runways, wheels turning.

"It's wonderful, David. I don't know how you do it."

"You know, I regret all the time I wasted. I should have been working, Ann, *really* working. It's possible this might earn us some extra money. Some of the shops in town might buy a few pieces. It's worth trying, don't you think?"

"Anything's possible," she said.

With dinner over, David was napping in front of the television. Ann found the old house stuffy in the warm late May night. Flinging open more windows, she saw that the stars shone brightly, lightning bugs flitted across the lawn, and the old house seemed to sigh in the breeze, either protesting the presence of new tenants or content to be of use again. She found it impossible to guess which.

Loneliness swept over her. Her life once had been so full; parties to attend, dinners to give, men to turn away with a laugh or a shrug. Now there was only time for survival, adjustment, change.

Long hours in a hospital beside David's bed, wondering whether or not he would live, had taken away the things she used to think were essential. She found that they had meant little.

She was a different person now. The old Ann Milan had died back there on that road four months ago. The new Ann Milan had steel in her, a touch of arrogance, and claws that she could bare in the interest of self-preservation if roused enough. But she was humbled, too, hurt, estranged from her old full, rich life, and she was lonely. Unbearably lonely.

The next day Ann selected her clothes with care. Out of the few expensive things she'd managed to keep, she made her selections.

She was blessed with long, dark hair that she let hang to her shoulders, a silky, rich mass that crackled under her brush. She had never indulged in heavy make-up. She had never needed it. She had clear, healthy skin and color to her cheeks and lips. Her eyes were direct and blue with fine flecks of silver. As she finished with a simple pair of earrings, copies of more expensive ones she'd sold for more than a thousand dollars, she wondered if Julian would even notice.

David assured her he could manage alone throughout the day, telling her he had more carving to do, pieces he wanted to finish. She drove away, telling herself that she must not worry about him.

As Ann drove the van toward the inn, she enjoyed the bright day, the drifting white clouds skimming the deep blue of the sky.

The inn sprawled comfortably beside the lake like a lazy giant stretching his legs and arms. The building had a rustic look with thick wooden shingles, brown siding and touches of native Vermont stone here and there at the front entrance. Large windows with tiny diamond-shaped panes gave back the brightness of the day. Tall, majestic pines and clusters of sugar maples reflected themselves in the lake nearby.

The inn was quiet this time of morning. The summer season had not really begun. Going past the desk at the lobby, she found her office dark. She went to open the draperies and let the day come inside. Julian's office was dark also, and she let the light in there, too, and began straightening the things on his desk.

"Ann, stop fussing," he said, coming into the room with his long, lion-like stride. "I can't stand fussy secretaries. If you straighten this up, I'll never find anything!"

She was stung by his coldness, his brusqueness. She left the room, closing the door behind her.

She turned her attention to her work. Julian had written checks for all the overdue statements, and she was getting them ready to mail out when he came striding to her desk.

"I'll be out most of the morning."

"Where can you be reached?"

"I can't."

"But what do I tell people? When do I say you'll be back?"

He moved away to the door. He turned back, his dark eyes unreadable. "You can say I'll be here at dinner time, but I don't want to be interrupted then either. You'll be dining with me, Miss Milan."

Her surprise couldn't have been more complete.

"I—I don't think so," she said, shaking her head.

He ignored that. "My suite. Seven o'clock. Tell the chef to sent the usual—but for two instead of one—"

And he was gone, and for once in her life Ann Milan had no answer.

Chapter Two

Dinner with Julian! Ann could scarcely think of anything else. But it was business, of course. She would have it no other way. If he thought there was any chance of it being anything more, he had another guess coming! She would not get involved with a man who still went jetting off to Europe to see his ex-wife!

Still, she couldn't deny that the thought of being with him kicked off an excited pulse; even if Julian was not for her, she still found him incredibly attractive.

There was no time to go home, for work at her desk kept her much later than she'd intended. She did what she could with a quick freshening up in the women's lounge.

Julian's living quarters were just down the hall

from the offices, although she had never seen them. It was exactly seven when she went to knock on his door. She hadn't seen him return and half-hoped he would not be there. But in a moment or two he flung open the door. Her heart dipped like a jet out of control.

"Come in," he said.

He had changed to a wine-colored, velvet smoking jacket and had removed his tie. A dark scowl cut across his handsome forehead as he motioned her inside, barely looking at her.

"I've a few things to go over with you, Miss Milan. And time is short. I thought we could combine dinner with our meeting."

Somehow she found her voice.

"Is this to be a regular thing?"

He gave her a mocking glance from his dark eyes. "Only on occasion. Strictly business, I assure you."

She flushed despite herself.

"I try never to mix business with pleasure, Ann. Even though it would be easy, even pleasant, to do so with such a lovely woman."

She lifted her chin, warning herself not to listen to any of this. It was just part of his charm. To bring herself under control she quickly stepped away from him.

Julian's suite was panelled in a rich glossy wood, the furniture was bold and masculine, the draperies of some heavy material. A small bar graced one side of the room, and sliding patio doors opened out to the lake. Near those doors a small table had been laid. Julian stepped behind the bar.

"Could I fix you a drink?" he asked.

"No, thank you."

He dropped ice into a glass with a cold clink and uncorked a bottle. As he sloshed the brown fluid over the ice, he gave her a sweeping glance, black eyes glittering. She flushed and turned away, imagining that his mouth quirked upward. She could not look. She would not!

She was keenly aware of his every motion and sensed when he turned to her. The walls seemed to be closing in. He took a step toward her, and she clenched her fists until the knuckles showed white. It was a relief to hear a knock at his door.

"That will be our dinner," Julian said.

One of the bus boys rolled in a cart, and the food was placed on the table. When he had gone, Julian held her chair.

His hands brushed her arms and a tingle set fire to her pulse. But he was all business.

"Autumn is our busy season. There are certain people who are regular customers. I try to roll out the red carpet for them. One of them is Mrs. St. Johns. Do you know her?"

"I remember her from last year. She's from New York, isn't she?"

"Yes. And she enjoys keeping us all on our toes. Try to go out of your way to make her feel welcome. Then there are a few other guests arriving next week. I'll give you a list in the morning. Mr. Bartlett sometimes has business correspondence—I allow him the use of my secretary from time to time. Please accommodate him. Then there is—"

He went on and on, naming names, pointing out the special favors she was to give them, until her head began to swim.

"I thought I was working for you," she said with a touch of annoyance in her voice.

"This *is* working for me," he said. He lifted his glass. "Dealing with the general public, even the uppercrust like Mrs. St. Johns, is not easy."

The food was up to the inn's usual high standards, but Ann barely tasted it. Julian, on the other hand, ate hungrily and seemed not to notice or care about her uneasiness. Now and then he appraised her, and once his hand had covered hers—but only to emphasize a point he was making.

They had reached dessert, a flaky pastry that was a specialty of the house. Julian devoured his and then got up to prowl around the room, searching for his pipe. When he found it, he filled and lighted it. Over the blaze of his lighter, he fired one jolting question.

"How could a successful man like your father get himself into such a mess?"

Anger flared as hotly as the flame over his pipe, and Ann was instantly to her feet, fists knotted. "I don't care to discuss my father! If you have no further business matters, I'll say good night."

"Sit down," he said. "Be calm. I wasn't being critical, just curious as to how it happened. I admired your father. I thought him one of the most likeable men I'd ever met. I was truly sorry to hear he'd had some trouble—"

His voice had taken on a different note. He sounded genuinely sorry. But could she trust that?

"I don't know, and I don't care to talk about it," she said.

"It seems you've had your share of rotten luck. I've seen David a time or two in his wheelchair. Some kind of accident, wasn't it?"

Her head was throbbing.

"I was driving too fast. I lost control. David was badly hurt."

"Is it a permanent injury?"

"Thank God, no. But it's going to be a long haul. And David frets. He so hates being helpless . . . dependent on me."

Julian's face was dark for a moment. "It must have been awful for both of you," he said quietly.

Ann had never shed a tear in public during all of this chaos, but now, under Julian's unexpected warmth, she felt hot tears searing their way down her cheeks.

He made a motion toward her, but stopped before he had. If he had touched her then, she would have collapsed in his arms and clung to him. Oh, how she wanted to press her face against his shoulder and be held in his arms, to forget all her doubts about him!

But she forced herself to choke back the tears, to stand straighter, to keep her voice as unemotional as possible.

"Sorry. I don't usually come unhinged like that."

"I think a walk in the fresh air is in order, Ann, and it's a lovely night for it."

Was this some kind of trap, or was he actually trying to be kind? Was he forcing her to remember another night when they had walked there, when he held her in his arms, crushing her against him? How could he have held her like that one moment and then disappeared the next with his ex-wife? A philanderer, what else could he be? He liked to cut it fast and loose with the women! Well, she wouldn't be one of those kind, no matter how attractive he was.

She walked ahead of him, but he quickly fell in step beside her, his pipe clenched between his teeth. He said nothing, but despite her misgivings about him, she was still acutely aware of his presence. It was all around her like some sweet fog, taking her breath away.

"I enjoy the lake at night," he said. "It's peaceful, don't you think?"

"Yes," she murmured politely.

"The inn gets hectic at times. You'll see after you've been here a few weeks," he said with a pleasant laugh. "Directly across the lake I have a little cottage hideaway."

She had to bite her tongue to keep from making a retort. Of course, he *would* have a hideaway.

"How does David get along with you away all day?" he asked.

She was surprised by the question and somehow resented his probing. "He manages. We both manage. I find it odd that you should care one way or another," she said coldly.

Another infuriating shrug of his shoulders. "I like to know a little about my employees. You seem defensive, Ann."

"Perhaps I am. If there are no more business matters to discuss, I'll say good night now."

For a moment she thought he was going to stop her. She set her shoulders in rebellion and turned away. With quick steps she hurried back to the inn, trembling inside. Her head began to ache.

She drove the van homeward far too fast and reminded herself to slow down. The lights were burning in the house when she reached it, but David didn't meet her at the door as usual. He was on the phone, and she caught only the last few words of his conversation. He hung up and swung his chair around to stare at her. His blue eyes burned with despair.

"You asked him to do that, didn't you, Ann?" he asked. "I thought you'd never beg for anything, from anyone!"

"I haven't the vaguest idea what you're talking about! And why are you so angry?"

David clenched the arms of his wheelchair so hard his knuckles showed white. "That was Julian Terrace on the line just now. He wants to see me tomorrow. He told me to come with you in the morning."

"Julian wants to see you? But why?"

"Something about a job. Ann, don't play innocent with me!"

She shook her head. "My dear brother, I haven't the foggiest idea what this is all about."

David blinked in surprise.

"Then he's serious? What could I do at the inn?"

"I don't know," she said, puzzled and startled by this turn of events. "I wish I did. Julian Terrace is a blackhearted devil whom I don't trust. Oh, David, we do get into some messes, don't we?"

He grinned, and the tension eased. He talked about it for nearly an hour, guessing what the job might be, obviously plainly elated at the prospect.

"If I could bring in some money, Ann, if I could help—" he broke off, cheeks flushed, eyes shining with hope. "I want to help you, Ann. You're carrying all the load—"

She ruffled his brown hair. "I seem to be bearing up. One thing about us Milans, David, we have guts. More than most people give us credit for."

"Amen to that!"

The next day David went with her to the inn. Breakfast was being served in the dining room as Ann pushed David straight back to the offices. Julian was already there, pawing through the papers on his desk. He looked up when he heard them.

"Come in, David," Julian nodded. "Ann, please close the door as you go."

She left David there in the lion's den, trying not to worry. David's hopes were so high. What if it didn't work, what if Julian let him down with a crash?

Their meeting lasted half an hour. Then Julian opened the door and called to her.

"Ann, put your brother on the payroll. He's going to take over the front desk from eight until five. Same hours as yours, same days off."

She met Julian's dark eyes with a stunned expression. He seemed to be daring her to find fault.

"But you have someone on the front desk already!"

"Correction. I *had* someone," he said. "I fired

him yesterday. I found him incompetent and a thief. I caught him with his hand in the till."

David was beaming. "He really thinks I can do it, Ann. And I'll work harder than anyone. I promise you both!"

"I've asked the night clerk to come in at noon today and show you the ropes, David. You might spend your time until then getting used to the place. And use any of the facilities you want. The pool—the gardens—you might enjoy the tennis courts, too."

"Yes," David said with a flush. "I—I used to play a lot of tennis."

"Some of our guests could probably use some pointers," Julian said. "Now, Ann, I have several letters."

David warmly shook Julian's hand, extended his gratitude again, and finally Julian eased him out of the room.

Ann closed the door behind her, notebook in hand, overwhelmed. Julian sat down behind the desk, all business.

"What you did for David just now, you can't know—I mean—it's not easy to say—" she broke off.

Julian gave her a quick, harsh scowl. "If he doesn't shape up within a couple of weeks, out he'll go, Ann. This is a business I run, not a charity, and if you have any ideas along those lines, forget them."

He was so cold and impersonal about it that all her warm feelings for him vanished. Swift anger took its place.

"You make that very clear," she said in a tight voice. "But if you break his heart, I'll never forgive you."

"He's a grown man. Stop babying him," Julian said curtly.

It was all she could do to sit there in her chair. She wanted to fling her notebook at him and walk out of the room never to come back. But he was the spider, he had her in his web, and she could not afford such a proud and grand gesture. Her fire had to smolder under self-discipline.

It was agony doing the letters. When they were finally completed, she put them on his desk, and he scrawled his heavy signature with a black pen.

"I'll be out of the office for a few minutes checking around. If you need me, page me on the intercom."

Then he was gone, and once he had left the room, she was struck by how empty it seemed. She caught sight of David out by the pool, and leaving her desk, she went to speak with him.

"David—"

He whirled his chair about eagerly. "Ann, you didn't tell me! Mrs. St. Johns will be checking in tomorrow. Do you realize who she is?"

Ann shrugged. "I met her once. A kind of bossy old gal, as I remember. Why all the excitement?"

David laughed and ran his hand through his brown hair. "She only happens to be an important patron of the arts! She's helped more than one struggling artist or sculptor. Maybe, well I know it's a big dream, but maybe she'll like the work I do, my carvings—"

Ann's nerves notched a little tighter. David was

riding on cloud nine. First the job at the inn and now this. But Mrs. St. Johns had never impressed her as being a woman easily influenced by anyone or anything.

"Ah, David, don't get your hopes up," she warned. "I'm not at all sure about her."

"Remember our motto," David said with a wink. "We'll lick 'em every chance we get."

She saw Julian coming toward them, walking with his quick stride. He moved with the grace of a sleek lion, his black mane of hair glossy in the sunshine. There was authority in every step, and when he neared them, he swept Ann away with his arm.

"Join me for a moment. Excuse us, David."

She managed to shake free but not before she was conscious of the long length of his thigh pressed against hers and the hard muscles of his arm around her waist.

He propelled her into the coffee shop where he ordered cups of hot tea laced with lemon. A lock of hair had fallen to his forehead. He leaned toward her with an air of impatience.

"Small catastrophe in the works," he scowled. "Mrs. St. Johns will be here about four o'clock. Ahead of schedule. Her suite is not quite ready, but I've sent the cleaning crews on the double. I want you to run some errands for me. Go to the florist, whichever one that you think is best. Purchase some very large and beautiful bouquets of flowers. Stop by the candy store, the one on the corner across from the bank—I can't remember the name of it—get a five pound box of chocolates. Oh, and one other thing, alert the Bow-Wow Kennels—"

He made a wry face at that. "She has a poodle. Boards him there," he explained.

"All this fuss for one woman? Seventy-five if she's a day, surely you must find it hard to be charming when there are more lovely women about."

A meaningful glance swept her way. "There are certainly more lovely women about. I'm looking at one right now."

She flushed and lifted her chin, ignoring the remark.

"I'll see to it that Mrs. St. Johns has the red carpet treatment," she replied stiffly.

"She's tough but sweet, too. If she were fifty years younger—"

"You'd kiss her down by the lake and then run off with your ex-wife!" she retorted.

A dull red crept up to his high cheek bones and black fury burned in his eyes. She didn't give him a chance to reply. Instead, she quickly walked away, leaving him to stare after her.

Mrs. St. Johns arrived a few minutes past four, and with her was a young blonde woman, very well dressed, who looked about with a disdainful air. Ann had not expected to see anyone but the old dowager. But Julian rushed to meet them, oozing charm.

"Well, well, Shelley Dickson. So we meet again."

He kissed the young woman, and she gave him a hug, whispering to him, making him laugh. Ann gritted her teeth. Apparently he knew Shelley and was eager to renew their relationship.

There was a fuss about getting checked in. Mrs.

St. Johns was bossing everyone right and left. David floundered at the desk, new to all of it, but Julian stepped in smoothly and took charge until they had gone to their suite.

David looked worried and flattened. "So, that's Mrs. St. Johns. I didn't imagine that she'd be like that!"

"Julian says her bark is worse than her bite. Besides, brother dear, you can win her over."

"Oh, sure," he murmured. But he didn't sound confident. David was going to stay late to learn more about running the desk. It was about nine o'clock when Ann returned to the inn to drive him home. He was still busy, so she decided to walk down to the lake. The night was balmy with a cool breeze coming in off the water. Trees rustled musically. The water danced under the stars, and with a ripple of shivering nerves Ann remembered standing here with Julian that night last autumn, being held hard and tight in his arms.

Now he was probably busy romancing Shelley Dickson. Their greeting had certainly been warm enough!

"Ann—"

She started and spun about with surprise. Julian stood there, bigger than life, his square shoulders blotting the sight of the inn behind him.

"You handled things with Mrs. St. Johns very admirably this afternoon. Thank you."

"All part of my job," she said crisply.

"I think you will impress her. And obviously David has been impressed by you. He adores you."

"We've shared some bad times lately. We're close."

"Why do I get this feeling you want to shut me out?"

"You have made it clear from the beginning, Julian, that I am your business secretary and nothing more."

He reached out and brushed a lock of her hair back from her face, his fingers tingling against her flesh.

"Does that mean we can't be friends?"

She seriously doubted he could be just friends.

"Why don't you find Shelley? I'm sure she can amuse you."

He muttered angrily, and his jaw turned rock hard. "You apparently think I'm after every woman I meet!"

"You *do* have a reputation—there is talk about you—"

"Well!" he said angrily. "If that's the case, I might as well live up to it!"

He reached out and pulled her close. She threw up her hands to stop him, but they were pinned between them as he masterfully crushed her to him. One arm locked her against his tall, lean frame while his other hand came up to her hair and pulled it back, forcing her to tip her face upward.

His breath was on her throat, his lips searing her vulnerable flesh, pressing to the wild hammering of her pulse.

I won't give in, she kept telling herself. *I won't let him know that I'm dying to give him back his kiss. I won't give in!*

But his mouth was working a kind of magic. His kiss was burning more intensely with every passsing moment, touching her eyes, her face, her lips, murmuring against her hair, seeking the hollow just above the V of her blouse.

She wrenched out of his arms.

"Let me go, Julian! How dare you force yourself on me!"

"I've heard about your reputation, too, Ann. You always leave a string of broken hearts behind you. You take a man as far as your bedroom door and then shut him out! You're a tease, Ann Milan!"

How dare he speak to her like that? Julian Terrace, the rogue, the rake, the man who still consorted with his divorced wife! And Shelley Dickson—and heaven knew who else.

"Can you deny it?" he demanded in a cold voice.

"I have never truly cared for any man!" she said through clenched teeth.

"Perhaps I am the one."

"Never!" she retorted.

He laughed at that, his mouth making a cruel smile. His intensity was a hot, dark fury that brought gooseflesh to her arms. He stroked her shoulders in a knowing way, stirring her, arousing her against her will. She felt as if she were the clay and he was the potter.

He held her more gently now, caressingly, his fingers fanning out across her back, pressing her to him. Desire was flaming inside again like a raging fire. His mouth claimed hers one last time before he picked her up in his arms and began to carry her away from the lake.

"Under the willows," he murmured. "It's cool and dark there—"

What was she doing? Had she gone mad? But she couldn't seem to stop him. He pressed his mouth to her throat, sought again the soft spot between her breasts, and in another moment she would have forgotten how she despised this man for his marauding way. She came to her senses in time.

"No! No!"

He dropped her to her feet, surprised, his fingers biting into her wrist.

"Tease," he swore at her. "You really are a tease!"

She tore away and started to run toward the house. As she did so, she saw Shelley Dickson, obviously looking for Julian. She called out to him.

"Julian, darling, where are you—?"

Julian emerged from the shadows.

"Something wrong, Shelley?" he asked.

She linked her arm through his, and in a moment they had walked away together. Once Ann thought they paused, and Shelley laughed provocatively.

Ann's heart wrenched. In a flash Julian had forgotten her. Another woman had called. He had forsaken her with no effort at all.

Face burning with shame at the way she had acted, she found her way back to the inn, avoiding any further sight of Julian. She was angry with herself for nearly succumbing to him. *It must never happen again!* When she gave her love, it would be to the man who loved her, and Julian would never love her. He was fickle, a ladies' man, playing a game. Taking what he wanted and then turning away. Ann didn't have much left but pride. She would hang on to that for dear life.

Chapter Three

If it hadn't been for David, Ann would never have returned to the inn the next day. But he was clearly so high on his new job that she couldn't risk anything happening to it.

She dreaded facing Julian, but there was no time for even the slightest awkward moment between them. He had been called out of town and was in a rush.

"Emergency. You'll have to hold the fort, Ann. I'll be away a few days."

He told her no more. But she could guess. He was off to see his ex-wife, again, flying to France to loll around in her fancy villa there! She was sickened by the thought.

During the time he was away, guests began to arrive in a steady number. Some for as short a time as a week or ten days, others for as long as three months. David was quickly adapting and loving every minute of his new job. Everyone liked him, and Ann's heart nearly burst with pride.

When Julian returned a week later, he was in a black mood. He looked tired. His voice was harsh and curt. Ann's sympathy went out to him until she spied the airline baggage tag dangling from his leather bag. There was no doubt now that he'd been to France as she feared.

"Any emergencies while I was away?" he asked.

"If there were, you certainly didn't seem to worry about them," she said crisply.

"That's why I have a competent staff," he replied, eyeing her belligerently. "What's got you riled?"

She gritted her teeth. "Did you have a pleasant time? One party after another, I suppose."

He flashed her a black, moody look. "Oh, sure, I had a great time!"

With that he went into his office with a slam of the door. It wasn't ten minutes later when Shelley Dickson appeared, apparently at his summons. She was leggy, wore her dresses one size too small, and swung her hips when she walked. Exactly the kind of woman Julian obviously preferred. A few minutes later they left together, Shelley hanging on to Julian's arm and batting her false eyelashes at him.

Ann tried to fight down the angry stab of jealousy, annoyed that it should matter what he did or who he saw. If only she didn't have to witness it all! But she was stuck here. Work. Yes, that was her salvation. She took her vengeance out on her typewriter keys, typing like mad.

For the next day or two Ann treated Julian coolly,

but if he noticed, it made no dent. Everytime she heard his quick step, her heart leaped. When he swept by her, she caught the fragrance of his after shave and tried not to remember the way he had kissed her and attempted to carry her away beneath the willows.

Still it was lodged in her heart like a sweet throb of pain. Then she would remind herself that she couldn't trust him. She would not be dallied with as he obviously dallied with other women!

There was another bad incident that raked along her nerves. She had just finished lunch and was crossing the lobby when she bumped into the Welbys.

"Why, Ann!" Mrs. Welby cooed. "I had heard you were here, but I didn't really believe it. Oh, my goodness, how awful for you! You must hate every second of it—"

Once Mrs. Welby had been an ideal of Ann's. No one was better dressed or held such a prominent social position in the area. Today Ann suddenly realized that she wore too much makeup, her jewelry was almost gaudy, and that she had a terrible whine in her voice.

"I rather enjoy it, Mrs. Welby. Nice seeing you again."

With that she had beat a hasty retreat to the front desk where David had witnessed the entire scene. "Don't let them bug you, Ann."

"They don't."

But it wasn't true, and he knew it. At her desk she choked back her tears and tried to work with cold, trembling hands. It didn't help any when she heard Julian open his office door. She sensed him leaning there, staring at her. It took all her willpower to ignore him. She longed to lift her head and drown in his dark eyes. If he so much as touched her, she would fling herself into his arms for comfort.

"Ann—"

"Yes," she said, drawing on all her self-control.

"I want you to go with me tonight. I must drive over to Wendall's Port," he said. "There's an old inn there—newly decorated—I want to see what they've done. I may want to make some changes myself. You can give me the woman's point of view."

She was shivering at the thought of being alone with him again, but her good sense came to her rescue. No way should she go with him.

"Sorry, I have plans tonight."

"Cancel them!"

She spun around to face him. His sardonic brow lifted and a squaring of his shoulders told her he would have his own way.

"You're infuriating! Am I expected to drop everything whenever you snap your fingers?" she lashed at him.

"When you work for me, you *work* for me. If that means doing things at the last minute, unexpectedly—yes, that's the way it is!"

She took delight in opening and slamming every drawer in her desk, not once, but twice, making as much racket as she could. Julian sat at his desk, calmly smoking his pipe, as if he'd suddenly gone deaf.

When she went to tell David what had happened, he raised an eyebrow and grinned. "Well, well!"

"David, will you kindly be quiet?" she asked, annoyed.

He laughed at that and reached out to rub his hand against her cheek. "It's okay, hon, I don't blame him. Why not spice up the evening with a gorgeous dish like you?"

They left the inn shortly before six, just as the dinner hour was starting. David gave her the victory sign on the sly, and she was nearly undone by it.

"We'll have dinner somewhere else. If I stay here, I'm sure to be detained," Julian told her.

The countryside this time of year was plush with greenery. The summer's night air was like a warm hand against Ann's face, and the rolling hills seemed to welcome her with eager arms. The quaintness of Vermont culture had been a part of Ann's life as long as she could remember. But tonight it seemed especially unique, and as they drove under a sky stained with the setting sun, she felt atune with the world. Without knowing it, she sighed, enthralled by the beauty of it.

"It's a lovely country," Julian murmured, as if he'd read her mind. "I'm not used to it, even after being here over a year."

"You're not a native Vermonter?" she said, trying to be polite.

"No. I come from New York."

"Family?"

"Not much anymore. One brother. If you find me

intolerable, Ann, you should know Denney," he said with a twinkle in his eye.

"No, thank you. One Terrace is quite enough!"

He flashed her a meaningful look. "Denney is very different from me."

"You mean he doesn't like wine, women and song?"

"Denney's very serious," he said with a harsh note in his voice. "Do you think I'm not?"

Visions of Shelley Dickson on his arm floated across her mind.

"You and Shelley are the talk of the inn."

He made a groaning sound and shook his head. "I suppose it would do no good to tell you that I've known Shelley for a very long time."

"You don't have to tell me anything, Julian," she said drily.

Her tone struck an angry chord. He stepped on the gas, and the car leaped. For a few moments he drove like this, as if taking out his exasperation on the car.

"If you're not hungry, we'll go on to the inn and dine there," he said with a cold tone.

She lifted her shoulder in a shrug. "You're the boss. I'm only along to advise you. Isn't that right?"

With a quick turn of the wheel he pulled the car off the busy highway and brought it to a squealing stop. He turned to her, taking her quickly by the shoulder. He gave her a little shake.

"Sometimes, Ann Milan, I could spank you. You're so damned uppish. You really have a chip on your shoulder, don't you? You act as if you've been asked to humble yourself to put in a little extra time on your job."

Her full sensuous mouth made a hard line. "I just want to keep our relationship clearly understood," she said evenly.

He laughed at that, a mocking, bitter sound. "Oh, you're doing that all right! Every time you look at me I feel as though I were a criminal."

"Shouldn't we be pushing on?" she asked coldly. "Half the night will be gone before we ever get there."

He muttered to himself, swearing, then his hands dropped away. With a roar he shot the car out into the lane of traffic again, the tires howling in protest. Ann smiled to herself in the deepening dusk. She had put him in his place this time. For once she had not wilted when he touched her.

Still she was acutely aware of him, of his hands on the wheel, the slope of his hard jaw, his heavy brows and shock of black hair. Now and then he sent her a smoldering look, but she lifted her chin a bit more and pretended that her pulse hadn't made an excited leap.

They glided through a small town and then stopped for a signal light. Julian shifted his body so he half-turned to her. His knee brushed hers in the small sports car, then his hand came out to shift gears, and she leaped away from his touch. She felt like a taper in a high wind, melting, melting, melting.

But eventually the sensation passed, and she took control of herself again. Julian was very quiet, watching the road intently, now and then staring at the gauges on the dashboard.

Abruptly he pulled off to the side of the road again.

"Alternator is discharging," he said. "I'd better take a look."

He raised the hood of the car and examined the engine with a flashlight. He came back, shaking his head, wiping his hands with a white handkerchief.

"I can't see anything wrong. At any rate, Wendall's Port is just a few more miles."

The thought of being stalled along the road, alone with him, was more than her churning heart could endure. Mercifully, in another few minutes they had reached Wendall's Port, but he drove on through the village.

"The inn is a few miles out of town."

"But what about the car?"

"It seems okay now. I'll call a garage and have someone check it while we're dining."

The old inn, formerly a working mill that had been renovated more than once, had obviously undergone still more changes. At first glance it seemed to Ann that a first class job had been done.

Once they were inside, Julian excused himself for a few minutes to use the phone. Then he came back, striding toward her. She'd be blind not to see how attractive he was. He gave her a smile that put her off guard. When he wasn't being a flirtatious Casanova, he was actually very nice.

His cool hand slid under her elbow as he guided her into the dining room. She was conscious of him so near. His chin grazed the top of her head as he held her chair.

Candles flickered with an intimate air. Beneath the table his knees bumped into hers. The candle-light reflected in her shining eyes and softened his hard chin. Their gaze met and held.

"You are indeed a lovely woman, Ann."

She warned herself that he probably said that to all women. But it was hard to ignore the timbre of his deep voice and the admiration in his eyes.

Just then the manager appeared, shattering the moment. He was a portly, balding man who hopped nervously from one foot to the other. His name was Sylvester Tice, and he wore thick glasses. He peered owlishly at everyone and everything. From the moment he saw them, he mistook Ann for Julian's wife.

"Oh, but—" she started to protest.

Beneath the table, Julian gave her a little kick. He flashed her a wicked grin as his eyes filled with bland amusement.

"Tell me, darling, don't you like these dishes?" he asked with a husbandly air. "Perhaps we could have something like them for *our* dining room."

She gave him a scorching, bewildered stare which prompted him to lift her hand to his lips and leave a kiss in her palm. Vainly she tried to pull away, but he held tight, smiling all the while.

When they left the table after dinner, Tice was waiting to take them on tour. Julian casually dropped his arm around her shoulder. The game had gone far enough! But he persisted in holding her firmly against him, bringing the color rushing to her face.

"It's very good of you, Tice, to take time to show us about," Julian said. "When I was here last January, you'd just begun renovating. I've been anxious to see the finished product. It looks very successful."

Tice rubbed his hands together gleefully. "Business *is* good. In fact, I've only one room left for the night. Now if you'll step this way—"

They toured the inn and heard all about the changes he'd made from one end of the place to the other. Ann had to admit that she was impressed, and Julian nodded thoughtfully several times. His dark eyes were missing very little, and he asked her to make a few notes.

Then Tice walked ahead, and Julian murmured that he'd spent far too much money.

"But it's so lovely!" Ann said.

"Lovely," Julian nodded. "But he'll never make back his investment."

They had reached the starting point of their tour. Tice was beaming proudly.

"Won't you stay for a nightcap?" he asked. "Oh, dear, I do believe it's raining!"

"A quick drink then," Julian said. "It's a long way back to Darshire, especially in the rain."

It was coming down in torrents. They heard it pounding steadily on the roof. Julian's dark gaze rested on Ann with an unreadable glitter. The room seemed too hot, too close. She didn't have the slightest idea why he had insisted on playing this silly game of husband and wife, and she was anxious to leave.

The drinks were gone. Tice lent Julian a raincoat to go out and bring the car up to the door. In a moment he returned.

"The car won't start. It's that damned alternator, I suppose."

"But I thought you called a garage when we first arrived!" Ann said with alarm.

"None was open. Is there an all-night gas station, Tice? Anyone who might help?"

"Oh, dear, dear! I'm afraid not. Everything closes very early in Wendall's Port."

"Then a cab," Ann said quickly. "So we can get back to town—"

"No cabs," Tice said. "And I can't drive you myself. My wife has gone with the car. Ah, but then you can be my guests for the night. I still have one room. Of course, that's it!"

Ann felt the blood drain out of her face. Julian's mouth twitched slightly. "That might be the perfect answer," he said. "Although we're without even so much as a toothbrush—"

"Ah, I can provide most everything. We keep a few items for our guests, you know." Tice bustled away.

Ann hissed to Julian between clenched teeth. "What are you doing? We are not going to share *one* room—"

"Come now, darling. Be nice about it. What else can I do?"

"You could sleep in the car!" she retorted.

"Sleep in a bucket seat? Have you ever tried that? Besides, we can't hurt poor Mr. Tice's feelings. He thinks he's just pulled the rabbit out of the hat. I guess he has at that—"

A key was dangled before their eyes. Tice escorted them to the room and unlocked the door. There was one large bed, a couch, the usual hotel furniture. Panic flooded Ann. Tice pushed toothbrushes, toothpaste and necessary personal items into Julian's hands.

"I hope you'll be comfortable. Good night."

The door closed behind them. Julian carefully twisted the key, locking them in. He turned back to her, tucking the key firmly in his pocket. She was trapped! The air suddenly seemed to disappear from the room. Her heart was thundering.

"Nothing to do but make the best of it," he said smoothly.

"I will *not* go along with this charade a moment longer!"

He gave her a cool, arrogant look. "You're going to feel terribly foolish if you try to get out of it now. If you objected, why didn't you stop it in the beginning?" he asked. He took a step toward her. Her throat tightened. "I don't think you wanted to, Ann. I think the idea of being my wife rather pleased you."

She lifted a shoulder with a haughty expression of disgust. "You overrate yourself, Julian."

"Is it possible you're frightened of me?"

She licked her dry lips. "Unlock the door," she demanded.

He laughed and shook his head. "Look at this. Can you see me in these!" he asked. He unfolded a very large pair of men's pajamas. "They must belong to Tice."

She tried not to smile, but it was hard to keep a straight face. If Julian put those on, he would look very funny indeed.

"Now this—no, no," Julian said, shaking his head. "This would never do. This isn't you at all."

The nightie was cotton, very plain and almost ugly. It must belong to Tice's wife.

"Far too dowdy. I can see you only in satin or silk, darling," Julian said. "But we needn't bother with these things. Come, Ann, why don't you relax? We might as well make the best of this."

"The key," she said, hand outstretched, eyes flashing.

"What do you propose to do? Walk in the rain all the way to Wendall's Port? That's more than five miles. And there's no hotel there. Nothing. You'd be there all night in the rain, alone—"

"Someone will drive me. I'll ask someone to—"

He was shaking his head, amusement flickering in his eyes. She swallowed hard, darting her glance around the room like a trapped animal. It was hard to breathe. The room seemed to shrink with every passing second.

"You're not going anywhere, Ann," he said.

He took a purposeful step toward her. She tried not to shrink back, but it was impossible to stand there and wait for him! He laughed and reached out to stop her.

"No need to run," he said smoothly, his eyes going to golden, narrow slits. "The other night, down by the lake, you were ready to come to me, Ann."

"No," she whispered. "No! You're wrong—"

"Oh, you ran like a frightened deer, but deep down, where it counts, you wanted to stay with me."

She was trembling. Gooseflesh rippled up and down her arms as he began to stroke her, soothing her. His fingers reached up to entwine in her hair. He was so close she could feel his breath against her face. The male scent of tobacco and after shave was overpowering.

"You want me, Ann."

"No! You think every woman is longing to throw herself at your feet, don't you? Not me, Julian!"

His fingers tightened in her hair, and he raised her chin with a doubled fist, forcing her to meet his eyes. "Still the tease, are you? Or is it that you're frigid, cold as ice? You're afraid to make love—"

With that he swept her into his arms. She was imprisoned against him. His mouth sought hers with quick, urgent hunger. She squirmed to be free, tried to fight him. It was useless. But she would not give in to this kind of man! She would never shame herself in such a way!

His mouth forced her lips open as his kiss grew more and more passionate. She was pressed to him, his body molded to hers. His hands reached down and thrust her harder against him, and desire shot through her, melting bones and reserve.

She broke away from his kiss and pressed her face

to his chest. Her arms ached to hold him, to caress and enjoy him. But she could not. She would not! She held herself rigid, and the more he tried to arouse her, the more she resisted.

Finally, with an angry mutter, he pulled away from her, his eyes coldly blank. She had momentarily defeated him.

"Have it your way, Ann!" he said with steel in his voice. "Making love to you wouldn't be much fun. You're an iceberg, I want a real woman in my arms—"

With that he moved away and began to empty his pockets. Then he removed his coat and loosened his tie. She stared at him in stunned bewilderment.

"You can sit up all night, if you want," he said. "I'm going to bed. But first, I'll have a shower—"

He had tossed out the key to the door, along with his billfold and change. But he saw her looking at it and snatched it up with a roguish smile.

"No chance, Ann. I'm darned if I'll let you run out of here and make a fool of both of us."

She was clutching at straws, desperate now.

"What about David? He'll be expecting me home. He will be waiting for me to drive him—"

He considered that for a moment. "I'll go down and phone from the lobby. I'll be the gentleman and stay away for fifteen minutes. You can use the bathroom first."

"Oh, how sweet of you!"

He opened the door and closed it behind him. The key grated in the lock. He had locked her in.

She paced the room. She must get out of here! She

considered climbing out the window, but saw there was no fire escape. The room was on the second floor. She was trapped!

Think. What should she do? How should she handle him? How could she keep him away from her? Perhaps she should undress down to her slip and pretend to sleep.

Nervously she hung away her dress and kicked off her shoes. Then she wished she hadn't. It might look like an invitation! Should she dress again?

There was no time, for she heard that familiar hard step in the hall. She dove for the bed and cowered under the sheet, closing her eyes, feigning sleep.

He came in and looked about. Then he stepped toward her and she braced herself, prepared to scream, to scratch and claw if he so much as touched her.

He was laughing softly, and she could sense his nearness. Then she took a deep breath as she heard him go into the bathroom and close the door.

In a moment he was singing loudly in the shower. She thought about dressing then, raced to try the door, and found it still locked. He had taken the key into the bathroom with him!

There was no escape! If she dressed now and sat primly in the chair, he would only laugh and make her feel the fool. No, she would show him she was not afraid of him. She would lie in the bed, eyes closed and sleep. She would not give him the satisfaction of besting her!

But it was easier said than done. Her throat had

gone dry. Her heart was beating so hard that she felt almost faint.

The door opened! *Don't look,* she thought. *Don't let him know you even realize he is around.*

But she peeked. What she saw nearly made her burst out in uncontrollable laughter. He was wearing the bottom half of Tice's pajamas, and they were far too big and too short.

But soon she forgot about that. She was conscious of his wide shoulders, the mat of dark hair on his chest, his incredible male magnetism. She swallowed hard. He was taking his time, prowling around the room as if it was the most natural thing in the world to be behind closed doors with a woman. For him it probably *was* natural! She must remember that. He was a blackhearted rogue who would toy with her and then forget her.

But try as she did, she couldn't seem to think about anything but the fact that he was here, with her, that he was very near.

She squeezed her eyes shut and tried to control her breathing. He knelt beside the bed, and his fingers touched her hair. She started. He began to stroke it gently.

"I know you're not asleep, Ann."

"Go away," she said in a stifled voice. "Please, go away—"

"No," he answered. "No—not until my so-called wife kisses me good night."

She sat up at that, real alarm coursing through her veins. Yet in the same moment she was quaking with desire, longing for his mouth on hers, wanting to hold him in her arms.

"No," she said again. But it was a very faint protest, hardly a protest at all.

His fingers caressed her bare shoulders. Then they crept up beneath her hair and lingered there. He bent toward her. She was frozen, stiff, unyielding. But he didn't let it stop him. She threw up her hands, fists knotted, to ward him off. But he was much too strong. He pulled her to him, and his mouth came down on hers, sensuous, hot, demanding. It tore the last of her resistance to shreds.

He sensed it immediately. Slowly, carefully, he began to arouse her, stroking her, pulling her close, his hands touching her until she ached with need and desire.

"Ah, Julian, Julian—"

"It's so easy," he murmured. "You want me as much as I want you. Tell me that you do—"

"No," she shook her head. "No!"

But his mouth was taking still another kiss, and in a moment she knew the last of her strength and willpower would be gone. She forced herself to remember the things she hated about him.

"No!"

She pulled away from him, eyes going cold and angry.

"I will not be one of your women!"

"Be quiet, Ann. You don't know what you're saying."

"Go to your ex-wife. She'll welcome you with open arms—or Shelley Dickson—or some other woman. But it won't be me! Never, never, never!"

She turned her face into the pillow and began to sob. In a few minutes she heard him stirring about the room, pulling on his clothes. Soon he had gone, slamming out of the room, the door banging angrily behind him.

She gave in to fresh sobs, realizing perhaps for the first time, how deeply she had fallen in love with him.

Chapter Four

Ann was shattered. Sleep would not come. She lay staring at the ceiling, tensing if she heard footsteps in the hall, hoping and yet fearing that Julian would come back. If he so much as touched her again, could she keep her anger at full tilt, could she restrain her own thundering emotions? For she loved him knowing full well that he was not pure of heart. He would never care for her as she cared for him.

The rain stopped sometime after midnight. Where had Julian gone? Perhaps he had camped in the lobby or tried to find comfort in the bucket seat of his car. Wherever he was, she wondered if he was thinking about her.

Ann finally drifted off to a fitful sleep. She awakened several times with a start only to drop off again. It was a bit later when she heard the door open, and Julian stepped in. Ann's heart began to thunder wildly. He stood for a moment, assessing the situation. Ann kept her breathing even and deep, feigning sleep.

At last he moved to the couch and sat down. With a groan he removed his shoes and stretched out.

"Oh, my aching back," he sighed aloud.

But the couch was not comfortable either, for he tossed and turned. His six-foot-two frame was clearly too long for it, and he lay with feet draped over the edge. After several minutes of this Ann was alarmed to see through half-closed eyes that he was approaching the bed. She suppressed a gasp.

Cautiously he stepped around to the other side to lay carefully down beside her. What was she to do? He stirred slightly, sighing deeply, as if in relief and contentment. Like a man very weary, he stretched out his long legs. He turned toward her, pillowed his head on his arm, and soon was asleep.

Ann's throat had gone parchment dry. She ached to move, but if she did, he would hear, perhaps reach out to her or speak. She was too bewildered, too spent and far too vulnerable to deal with that now.

Sleep was truly elusive. Once, when she was certain he was deeply asleep, she dared move and turned over to her back. He stirred as well, muttered something, and flung his arm across her. Alarmed, she tried to move away, but convulsively he curved his arm as if to hold her there beside him. Still he slept. She was positive he didn't know what he was doing. She was pinned beneath the weight of his arm. She simply could not bear this! Quickly she turned her back to him. But his arm only moved to accommodate the motion and settled firmly around her waist.

She dared not put her hand over his. There was no murmur, no movement, just his steady, even breathing. Odd, how quickly all of this felt so right. She was here, lying in the arms of the man she loved, even though he didn't know it, and she had never felt so good about anything before.

She enjoyed his body warmth, the heaviness of his arm, the touch of his fingers. How she could have fallen asleep again, she didn't know, but when she awakened the next time, she found she had snuggled against him. She had turned to him in her sleep, and he had stretched out his arm, making a pillow of his shoulder. He had wrapped arms and legs around her. His shirt had come unbuttoned, and she had slipped her hand inside to come to rest against his bare chest and the heavy mat of black hair.

She lifted her head with a start and found his eyes closed, his breathing deep. There was daylight beyond the windows! Quickly she untangled herself from him, snatched up her things and fled to the bathroom, locking the door behind her.

She stayed a very long time, staring at her flushed cheeks in the mirror. Doing what she could with her hair, using makeup from her purse, she finally finished and, taking a deep breath, she pulled open the door.

He was gone!

"What a relief!" she sighed.

There was a note on the desk.

"Tice is driving me to Wendall's Port to locate a mechanic. Have breakfast, and I'll be back as soon as possible."

It was signed Julian. But there was a P.S.

"Did you know you talk in your sleep?"

Hot and cold washed through her. So he had not been asleep all the time! And what foolish things had she said? She crumpled the note and then smoothed it. Quickly, with almost a sense of guilt, she tucked it away in her purse for safe keeping.

The lobby was empty, the dining room nearly so, for it was very early. The coffee cleared her head, and her illusions came into perspective. Shame swept over her. How could she have permitted herself to lie in his arms? How could she have been so out of control? It must not happen again!

The car was repaired by nine o'clock. Julian came to find her. He stood for a moment, staring at her with his black gaze.

Could he tell that her pulse was hammering with excitement at the mere sight of him? She hoped not. The memory of their night together stained her cheeks with a flush of red. She lifted her head haughtily and met his gaze.

"Is the car ready?" She put ice in her voice, snobbishness to her lifted chin.

His eyes flickered with answering anger. "You'll be happy to know we can now be on our way."

He was coldly aloof, his black mood surrounding them like an impenetrable fog. The car started with a roar, and they drove off with a spin of the wheels. Julian paid strict attention to his driving and scarcely spoke on the way back to Darshire. Ann sat like a lump beside him, looking straight ahead, aching with hurt and bewilderment.

Terrace Inn at last! Ann went immediately to find David. He was busy behind the desk, sorting mail for the guests. He looked up with a grin.

"Well, so you two finally got back," he said, giving her a mischievous grin that did nothing for her morale.

"How are things going?" she asked.

"I have news. Big news. Mrs. St. Johns and I had a great talk. She's really a very sweet old gal, Ann. And guess what! She's asked me to bring some of my work for her to see. Tonight. Maybe you'll help me select the right pieces—"

"Of course."

"You don't seem to be in the best of moods," David said with a searching glance. "Was the outing a bust?"

"Worse than that. A disaster," she muttered.

She didn't want to explain, so she whisked away to the office. It was going to be an unbearably long day. She attacked the work with all the vigor she could muster. Julian came in a few minutes after her, still black with anger, and strode past her desk without a glance slamming the door behind him.

Most of the day he stayed behind that closed door, having room service bring his lunch on a tray. She could hear him on the phone. She could tell from the tone of his voice that he was having a bad day, too.

The day was destined to be even worse, for Shelley Dickson, willowy, cool, and lovely, appeared at Ann's desk. Another of Julian's toys?

"Hello there!" Shelley said brightly. "Is the man in? I must see him."

"I think he's on the phone," Ann said, hoping to discourage her.

"But it's *very* important. Mrs. St. Johns has sent him a message, and I am to deliver it personally—"

If Mrs. St. Johns said jump, Julian jumped. As did everyone else around here.

"I'll tell him you're here," she said.

She went to tap lightly at Julian's door and stepped in. He had just hung up the phone and was scrawling some figures on a pad in front of him.

"Yes. What is it?" he asked, barely glancing her way. His indifference to her was like a slap.

"Miss Dickson wants to see you. Urgent, she says. Something about Mrs. St. Johns."

"Blast!" Julian said with a long sigh. "Okay. Send her in."

Shelley was closeted with Julian for more than half an hour, and it wasn't long before she could hear them laughing together. Ann couldn't bear it. She stormed away from her desk in pursuit of a cup of hot, strong coffee.

She ached to go home, to leave the inn and Julian behind. But to make matters still worse, Mrs. Stevenson implored upon her to fill in for her as hostess for the dinner hours.

"If you would, Ann—"

She sighed and nodded. "Of course."

"Bless you—"

It meant going home, taking a quick bath and changing into a hostess gown. Worst of all, it meant spending several more hours under the same roof with Julian Terrace!

That evening David returned to the inn with Ann to visit Mrs. St. Johns in her suite. He was riding on cloud nine, and Ann tried to caution him about it.

"I've got a feeling about her, Ann. It's going to be okay!"

The dinner hours at Terrace Inn were always busy at this time of year. But when Ann looked over the reservation list, her heart dropped to her shoes. She saw at least half a dozen familiar names. The uppercrust of Darshire, her old so-called friends! After the scandal involving her father, most of them had dropped her. Only Tina Phillips, touring in Europe right now, had stuck by her.

Ann took a deep breath. She had to get through the evening and nothing anyone said or did was going to wilt her down. But she hadn't counted on seeing Julian with Shelley on his arm.

Julian had never looked more handsome. He wore a light summer jacket and dark trousers. A bright tie softened his lean, hard jaw. Beside him Shelley was especially lovely, her blonde hair shimmering, her lips cool and upturned pleasantly. She clung to his arm possessively. Ann's head began to ache anew.

"My private table, Ann," Julian said with a brooding look.

"Of course," she said crisply.

She led the way, conscious of Julian and Shelley directly behind her. She watched as Julian held Shelley's chair and bent to whisper in her ear. Whatever he said was outrageously funny, for Shelley laughed shrilly.

"Ah, you devil!" Shelley cooed.

Ann, resisting the urge to hurl the big shiny menus at both of them, placed them on the table. Julian's dark eyes were smoky and dangerous as they met her glance.

"Enjoy your dinner," she said coolly.

"Oh, we will," Shelley sighed, never taking her eyes off Julian. "I love this table. So private, Julian—"

Julian turned his gaze away from Ann to smile at Shelley. Ann left them there together. Every time she seated someone, she was aware of them huddled close, the candle flickering between them. Once Julian's gaze swept critically in her direction, but it was as a manager, not a man. He probably hoped she would make some horrible mistake so he could find fault. Perhaps even fire her.

That idea sent cold chills down her back. She must have this job, and that meant being near him. How ridiculous to let herself be caught up in such a web of love. He was only a man, she kept telling herself. But her heart cried out that he was the *only* man she wanted, the only one in her life.

She was relieved when Julian and Shelley finally left the dining room, but she could not help wondering how they were spending the rest of the evening.

The dinner hour passed busily, and she was free to go at last. She went to find David. The night clerk told her that he was still in Mrs. St. Johns's suite. Ann decided to go up herself and perhaps bolster David's confidence.

When she was outside the door, she pressed the bell, and in a moment Mrs. St. Johns was there.

"Ah, Ann, do come in. I've been having the most fascinating conversation with your brother. And his carvings—I'm really impressed!"

She looked at the older woman to see if there was any insincerity in her voice, but could detect none. Mrs. St. Johns seemed excited. The more she talked, the more animated she became. David sat in his wheelchair, hunched forward, hanging onto her every word.

"She thinks I have a real future, Ann. I hope she's right."

Ann assured him that she was. Mrs. St. Johns had even offered to buy one of the pieces for her own private collection and had written a handsome check for it.

"You've been very generous, Mrs. St. Johns," Ann said.

"For goodness sakes, don't make me feel patronizing. I actually *stole* it! I predict in a few years that it will triple in value, perhaps even more than that—"

"You see what I mean?" David asked with a happy laugh.

"I do," Ann said, relieved that it had worked out so well.

"I wonder what is keeping Shelley," Mrs. St. Johns said with a trace of annoyance in her voice. "I had no idea she would take such a long dinner hour."

"She was with Julian," Ann said. "I assume they're old friends."

The dowager lifted her shoulder in an irritable shrug. "Friends, you say? More than that, I suspect. But I told Shelley to be back here no later than nine o'clock and look at the time. Sometimes that girl is so inconsiderate! I depend on her for so many things—but there—I shouldn't be talking about her like that."

"And we should be going," Ann said quickly. "David—"

"Yes. Of course. How can I thank you, Mrs. St. Johns?"

"No need. I'll see you tomorrow, David. Why don't you leave your carvings until then? I'd like to study them further."

Ann followed David out of the apartment and down the elevator. David was suddenly tired. She knew from the way he leaned back, eyes closed for a moment, that the evening had been a strain.

"I have to tell you," he said with a tired sigh. "That old girl is no one's fool."

When they reached the ground level and the elevator doors swung open, Ann saw Julian. He was at the desk, talking with the night clerk. He spun around to face her with a brow quirked upward. How superior he acted!

"I thought you'd gone home."

"We're on our way now," David said.

Julian straightened and thrust his hands deep into the pockets of his jacket.

"They tell me that now you're able to maneuver in the water, David," Julian said.

"Yes," David nodded. "It's good therapy. Has Ann been talking—"

"No," she said quickly, coolly. "I try to keep our personal lives away from the inn."

Julian's lips turned upward in a scornful smile. "I only wanted to tell David that he's welcome to use the pool here anytime—"

David flushed. "No. I'd rather not make a spectacle of myself and embarrass both myself and your guests."

"I see. Of course. Thoughtless of me. Well—then, perhaps at night—the pool is seldom busy then and yet the water is warm."

David nodded. "That sounds like a possibility! Thank you, Julian."

"Not at all. Ann is always welcome to the pool, too. I'm not sure I've made it plain that both of you are to use and enjoy all the facilities here."

How cold he was! How businesslike. But she wouldn't give him the satisfaction of knowing that the offer to use the pool was deeply felt. It was a perfect answer for David, for he badly needed such therapy.

On the way home David talked only about Julian.

"Cool as a cucumber, isn't he?" David asked. "But a decent sort, nonetheless. I like him so much more than I thought. And I'd like to use the pool, provided you could go in with me, Ann."

"Sure. Maybe tomorrow evening."

David gave her a long look. "What happened last night at Wendall's Port? You haven't been yourself since—"

She gave him a saucy grin and dismissed it with a shrug. "Nothing, darling. Nothing."

David let the subject drop. But she hadn't fooled him. Even though they had grown very close since the accident, this was something she couldn't share with him. It was too private, too personal, too deep.

She slept that night from sheer emotional fatigue. She tossed and turned and woke up feverish, Julian's name on her lips. Oh, to have him beside her now, his arms around her. When had she fallen so deeply in love with him? The ball last autumn? Yes, it had begun then.

There were shadows under her eyes the next morning when she dressed for work. She chose a simple white dress that accented the slope of her jaw, the soft hollow of her throat. She hung a single silver chain there with a locket that her father had once given her. White pumps, sheer nylons, a swish of her skirt, a toss of her hair and she felt ready to tackle the world, even Julian Terrace.

When she reached the office the next morning Julian was not there. He came moments later. She knew instantly that his black mood had gone. He wore casual slacks and a polo shirt that spanned the breadth of his shoulders. Ann tried to suppress her feelings, but, oh, to lay her head on that shoulder once again!

"I'd like a couple hours of your time," he said coolly. He fondled his pipe and studied her from beneath his dark brows. "I want to do some work at my cottage across the lake. Decorating—as you know, I'm not very good at such things. I'd like your opinion."

"I'm a secretary, Julian, not an interior decorator!"

He ignored that by pushing back the cuff of his sleeve and glancing at his watch. "Half an hour," he murmured. "I'll meet you in the lobby."

With that he walked out of the room, pipe clenched between his teeth, leaving her trembling at the thought of being alone with him again. She worked up her anger, tried to seethe with it. He was so darned superior, certain that whatever he demanded she would do! *Working for Julian Terrace was certainly not a routine eight-to-five job,* she thought wryly.

On the other hand, she *was* curious about the cottage, and it wasn't likely after the night at Tice's Inn that he would want to touch her again. Or so she told herself.

He was already in the lobby half-an-hour later when she left the office to find him. He left word with David where they were going and gave him the number.

"Phone only in case of a real emergency. And don't reveal that number to anyone."

"Got you," David nodded.

It took fifteen minutes to drive around the lake to the cottage. It was nearly hidden, nestled deep into the trees. It was rustic, painted brown and shingled with rough shakes. The windows were long and narrow. The entire cottage was faced with a screened-in porch that looked out to the water. Comfortable lounge chairs had been turned over or leaned against the wall.

Julian unlocked the door.

"Come in, Ann."

She began to tremble at the thought of being alone with him. But with a lift of her chin she walked through the door, trying not to be aware of him as she brushed past him, her shoulder touching his chest.

The cottage was rustic with furniture of native, polished pine. There was a glossy paneling on the walls and throw rugs on the floor. The fireplace was made of rugged stones. Pewter candlesticks sat on the roughly hewn oak mantle.

He arched a brow at her. "Pretty bad?"

"I think it's perfect for its setting!"

He laughed, pleased. "But you haven't seen the kitchen!"

She had to agree that it needed help and needed it badly. She made a few suggestions such as new cupboards, a new sink and more built-in appliances.

"And bright colors. If I were you, I'd cut a sliding patio door, build a patio just outside with a redwood deck. Casual furniture there, a big sun umbrella— you know the sort of thing I mean."

He was listening closely, his gaze never leaving her face.

"Maybe you could put all of that into a memo for me," he said. "I'll get some estimates."

"Perhaps it wouldn't be worth it," she pointed out. "It's bound to be costly."

"Cost is no object. You haven't seen the bedroom," he said. "I'm sure you'll have suggestions for that."

Her cheeks burned as she remembered another bedroom, the one they had shared one rainy night.

He was watching her closely, an amused look on his face. She lifted her chin and marched into the bedroom. It was barely adequate. Both it and the bath were a sorry state. She quickly made suggestions while he stood about, arms folded, watching her with narrowed eyes.

What was he thinking? Was he remembering as well?

"I've seen everything. I think I should get back to the inn now," she said stiffly.

He lifted his lips into a smile. "You seem nervous being here."

She couldn't reply. His laugh was short and unsettling. "Afraid?" he asked.

"Why should I be?"

His look had flashed into one of tender passion, and it rocked her so that she stumbled back from him.

"You know why," he said.

"I—I must go," she said.

She hurried away, half expecting him to detain her, but relieved when he didn't.

"I'll expect you to make the final choices," he told her.

"I'm sure you have your own ideas!" she said with a scorching glance. "Especially about the bedroom."

He was still laughing as she walked away to the car and climbed in. In a moment he came to join her, and without a word drove her back to the inn.

She did not see him again for the rest of the day. When she had given David his supper at home, he suggested they return to the inn for a swim in the pool. It was the last thing she wanted to do, for she wasn't up to another encounter with Julian. For David's sake, she agreed.

The pool was clear, the water tepid from the afternoon's warm sun. David could manage himself enough that he got into the water with little assistance, simply by sliding off the edge of the pool. Ann was there to watch him, but David's arms were very strong. He moved in the water much better than she had dared to hope during his long, tortuous days in the hospital. But in half an hour he'd had enough and wrapped himself snugly in his terrycloth robe.

"You go ahead and swim, Ann," he said. "You've been so busy with me, you've had no chance—I'll go to the coffee shop and have something there. One of the waitresses is a friend—"

"Ah, ha!" she teased.

David laughed and rolled away in his wheelchair. He was using his crutches now, but tired easily. Ann sighed as she watched the wheelchair round the corner. Once he was safely inside, she was tempted by the high dive. Her white swimsuit showed off her lithe figure. She hadn't played tennis and gone riding and swimming in the Country Club swim meets for nothing. Her suit showed off nearly perfect legs, well-shaped arms and firm, round breasts. From the high diving board she sucked in a deep breath, poised on her toes, and leaped. She made a perfect dive, split the water with ease, touched bottom, and came up. It was always exhilarating, that brief moment in mid-air. It was a release, a way of combating restlessness, and for a little while she felt like her old self, on top of the world, the invincible Miss Ann Milan, the life of the party.

She made three such dives and then began swimming the length of the pool, back and forth. She could hear the music from the dining room. Miraculously she had the pool all to herself. She didn't know exactly when she knew someone was watching her. Slowly she began to search the shadows, and then she saw him. He stood leaning against the wall of the inn, casually, as if he were indulging himself in some rare and unexpected sight.

"Please, come here," he said quietly.

She wanted nothing more than to get out of the pool and run for her life.

"I'm off duty," she said evenly.

"I'm quite aware of that," he murmured. "Come here."

She swam toward him, climbed the ladder, and shook the water from her face. Her wet suit clung to her body, revealing every curve. She had never felt it was too revealing before. Now, beneath Julian's probing eyes, she felt as if she were stark naked.

"Where did you learn to swim like that?" he asked.

"I've always swum like that."

"Part of your breeding, no doubt," he said.

His fingers were inching under her bathing cap, and he flung it off and to the ground. Her hair came tumbling down to her shoulders, soft and dry, scented.

"That's better," he said.

She couldn't move, couldn't resist letting his

fingers caress her arms, moving up to her shoulders. Then he pushed down one of the straps of her suit so that it slipped over her arm. He bent his head, and his lips burned the little crease the strap had cut. His lips followed the line of her shoulder, slowly, caressingly, to sink into the soft hollow of her throat. She stood stiff and unrelenting.

"Let go, Ann," he murmured. "Come now, don't be like this."

"Julian, don't! What can it mean? What purpose does it serve?"

"Let's not talk about the why and wherefores of anything. Why spoil a moment like this?"

With a swift motion she was crushed in his arms, held hard and tight against him, and his mouth was on hers, demanding, harsh, eager, seeking. This time she couldn't stop her own arms from going around him. She held him, smoothing her hands along his shoulders, touching his thick, dark hair, tangling her fingers in it as he kissed her for long, long moments.

"Julian—darling—are you out here?" a voice called.

Ann stiffened in his arms and tried to pull away, but he kept her tight and hard against him. "Shh! Don't move, she won't see us."

"But it's your dear, sweet Shelley," she retorted.

"Shut up," he said in her ear. "Just shut up. Even if she sees us, she won't know it is us in the dark."

"Oh, so that's it! You don't want her to know that you're with someone else—"

She yanked out of his arms. In the dim shadows she saw the set of his jaw, the flashing eyes. She ran to the edge of the pool and dove in, making a loud splash. Then she swam furiously, kicking water far and wide. She heaved herself out of the pool on the far side, snatched up her things, and ran toward the dressing rooms. Behind her she could hear Julian laughing softly. The sound of his mirth carried across the pool, taunting her, ripping her nerves to shreds. But Shelley had heard him, too, and was going to him, softly calling his name.

Chapter Five

Surprisingly, things settled down at the inn, for Ann soon learned one basic fact about Julian. While in the office he did not mix business with pleasure. At his desk he was a different man. He looked at her only as a secretary. Never once by a glance, a wink of an eye, or a gesture did he betray that they had shared some passionate moments together.

Ann forced herself to forget them. The job was a challenge, and it took all her wits to keep her head above water. Julian was a typical boss. There were days when he piled work on her desk and wanted it all done instantly. Other times she might not see him all day long and still other times he was thoughtful and considerate.

"Ann!"

She was used to his call now, at once demanding, often on edge. She could recognize the different tones of his voice, and this time knew that it meant to come on the double and close the door behind her.

The moment she entered the room, she saw all the folders, carpet and drapery samples, and knew that he'd begun work on the cottage across the lake.

"The interior decorator gave me these yesterday and said I should pick out what I want. My word, Ann, I don't know what goes with what—"

"The poor helpless male," she said lightly.

He grinned at that, the particular smile that always caught her off guard. "That's why I have you. What do you think?"

She looked carefully at all he had. It was too difficult to select things like that.

"The light and the surroundings are so different at the cottage. Why don't you take them over there and see how they strike you?"

He scowled. "Can't. Business meeting at three. Why don't you go over later this afternoon? Take all this stuff with you—"

He shoved the untidy heap in her direction. With a nod she scooped up the samples. "All right. If you want. Have the workmen started?"

"Yes. I hope you'll see some good progress. Give me a full report when you come back—"

"Sure."

She had no more than reached her desk when her phone rang.

"Ann, Mrs. St. Johns. I was wondering, do you have a few minutes? I'd like you to come to my suite."

"Yes, of course, Mrs. St. Johns. I'll be right there."

David was at the desk when Ann walked by, but he was busy with a guest. She had no idea why the old dowager wanted to see her, but whatever it was, she was expected to keep her happy and to abide with all her wishes.

At the door to the suite Ann took a deep breath. If Shelley Dickson was in there—well, she'd have to be nice to her, even if it set her teeth on edge. As Mrs. St. Johns's companion, Shelley rated the same V.I.P. treatment.

Ann knocked lightly, and in a moment the door was opened to her.

"Nice of you to be so prompt, Ann. Please come in. I've asked room service to bring us something cool to drink. Sit down."

Ann scanned the suite quickly, and was relieved to see no sign of Shelley. Mrs. St. Johns wore a stylish blue dress, and her white hair was piled to the top of her head. Jewels sparkled on her hands. Ann was glad to see that the carving she had purchased from David had been given a prominent place in the room.

"It is quite good, you know," she said.

Ann turned back to her with a smile. "Yes, I think so, too, but I'm not an expert on such things."

"I want to talk to you about David."

"What can I tell you?"

Mrs. St. Johns was interrupted by the arrival of a food cart. The bus boy brought it into the room and left with a healthy tip in his hand. He flashed a sly smile of satisfaction in Ann's direction. Mrs. St.

Johns made a little ceremony out of pouring the glass of iced tea.

"David is young—probably twenty-three?" she asked.

"Twenty-two," Ann said.

"How long has he been—"

"In a wheelchair? Not long. We were involved in an auto accident last January. Since then, David has had almost no use of his legs. He is just beginning to manage on crutches, but it is still much easier in the chair."

Mrs. St. Johns looked sad and reached out to pat Ann's hand. "He tells me how wonderful you've been."

Ann flushed. "I was driving, Mrs. St. Johns. I've never been able to forget that. I feel it is my fault—"

"You have no family?"

"No. Not since my father died. David and I have been alone."

"I've become very interested in him, you know. I must confess, I have my own selfish reasons. You see, Ann, I lost my son years ago. Now and then I see things in David that remind me of Phil."

"Oh!"

"I hope you don't mind."

"He is going through a hard time now. I think it's the best thing in the world for him! And he admires you, Mrs. St. Johns."

"How sweet of you to tell me, Ann," Mrs. St. Johns beamed.

"There's only one thing—"

Mrs. St. Johns's eyes sharpened. "Yes?"

"About his work—his carvings. He's really very

excited because you've shown some interest. I don't want it to be a false interest—"

"My dear, it isn't! I feel David has great potential."

Ann took a deep breath. "I'm glad to hear that."

"As a matter of fact, I've a few ideas I'd like to discuss with Julian Terrace. But I seldom find him unoccupied. So perhaps I can reach his ear through you. You see, I'm interested in all forms of art; paintings, sculpture, carvings, local craft—everything. I would like to sponsor an art show this summer here at the inn. I think it would be fun, don't you?"

"It's a nice idea," Ann nodded. "I'm not sure about Julian—"

"He's a gracious host. I'm sure he'd lend us the lobby. We could set up exhibits, invite the local people, advertise it in New York—make it quite an affair. It might even turn out to be great! Would you implore him to consider it?"

Ann laughed. "You're very ambitious. And, of course, I'll talk to Julian about it. I'm sure he'll be in touch with you soon."

"Fine, fine. And of course I want David to display all of his work."

"He'll be delighted!"

"Let's not tell him about it until it's all set. Why risk disappointing the boy? Something might prevent it—"

Ann nodded. "Thank you, Mrs. St. Johns."

"Not at all," she said with a warm smile. "I think this summer at the inn is going to be better than last. I always enjoy coming here, but I'll have to confess,

I miss the excitement of New York. This will be great fun, Ann."

Ann said goodbye and left the suite. At the elevator she had the misfortune of coming eye to eye with Shelley Dickson.

"Well, hello," Shelley said.

She was especially lovely today, almost shimmering in her blondeness. It annoyed Ann to see the superior way she assumed, as though Ann were someone beneath her.

"I wish you'd tell the maids to do our suite earlier in the day," she said airily. "They're getting to be quite sloppy about their work."

"I'll take it up with the housekeeper," Ann said smoothly. "Sorry if there's been any inconvenience."

"Would you tell Julian to please call me?" she asked.

"He's going out," Ann said, stepping on the elevator. Just as the door closed, she added, "With me—"

She was rewarded with a frown on Shelley's pretty face and two red spots of furious color. Ann laughed all the way down to the lobby, startled that she had told such a lie.

She had intended to go at once to the cottage, but one thing led to another. Delay followed delay until it was nearly four-thirty when she was able to leave. She warned David she would be late.

"Doesn't matter. Mrs. St. Johns has invited me to have dinner with her. I'd like to stay and join her. Okay?"

"Great! I'll eat here, too, when I come back."

She blew David a kiss and hurried away. Julian had lent her his key, and she drove along the lake road, not hurrying, enjoying the day. The sun was still hot, and the thought of the lake was very pleasant. Even though the inn was on the lake, too, it was kept icy with air conditioning. Ann preferred the summer days as God had made them, warm, sunlit, with clear skies and drifting clouds. Tall, green trees offered cool shade and the rippling water of the lake lent its breath to a natural coolness.

When she reached the cottage, she found the workmen had already gone, if they had been there at all. Letting herself inside, she found that they had done very little. Julian would not be pleased to hear this. It didn't take her long to examine the carpet and drapery samples and to come to her own personal choice. That done, she knew she should return to Terrace Inn. But it was already late. Office hours were over. David was having dinner at the inn. The lake called to her. She wandered down to the water, and sitting on the pier, arms wrapped around her knees, she watched the sun disappear over the top of the trees. A golden light was dropping around her, geese flew overhead, a boat went by in the distance, creating a wake of sweeping waves against the pier. She stretched back on the sun-warmed planks of the dock, drifting with the red-rimmed clouds, losing herself in the sky.

The lake was irresistible. She had an urge to go in the water. But she had no swimsuit. Looking about, she knew that the cottage sat on an isolated spot, that if she went behind the trees a few steps away, she could strip off and drop unseen into the water.

94

She hid herself, quickly pulled her dress over her head, followed with her slip, then removed her pantyhose and bra. The warm air touched her flesh, and with a giggle, feeling somehow naughty and very, very young, she walked out into the water and began to swim.

She splashed around happily, diving under to study the bottom of the lake, surfacing to shake her head like a seal, and then making long, unhurried strokes, the water caressing her like a lover. This time of day was especially beautiful. She felt as if she were part of the lake and sky; one with the trees stirring in the breeze.

Suddenly she was conscious of not being alone. She looked toward the shore and saw with a start a lone figure standing with folded arms, watching her.

It was Julian! He lifted an arm to wave and motioned for her to come out.

"Go away!"

"Never," he called back.

She swam a little closer. Worst of all he'd found her belongings. Carefully he bent down and draped them over his arm, a piece at a time. The heat of her body surely raised the temperature of the lake by a few degrees.

"Why don't you come out and join me?" he asked teasingly.

"Julian, please—leave my things—and go!"

He shook his head in a maddening way. "Not a chance, Ann. I'll give you your clothes if you want to come and get them—"

She shivered in the warm air. What on earth could she do? There was nowhere to hide, no place she could escape to. Only the lake. The water mercifully hid her nakedness from him.

He sat down on a fallen log and calmly lit his pipe.

"How is the water?" he asked. "It must be very good today. You looked as though you were thoroughly enjoying yourself."

"How dare you intrude like this! How could you sit there and spy on me? Of all the mean, horrible things to do!"

He laughed. The sound of his mirth floated across the water to her.

"I'm really not *doing* anything. Just enjoying the day—" he paused with a rakish grin. "And the sights."

She flushed, her body flaming with still more embarrassment. But she couldn't stay in the water forever.

"Please, Julian, have a heart—it's going to get cold out here before long."

He blew a smoke ring. Then, finally, with an elaborate sigh, he laid her things down and got to his feet.

"All right, my sweet. I'll wait for you at the cottage and fix you a toddy against taking a chill."

Even then she wasn't sure she could trust him. She back-paddled, waiting for him to get out of sight. Then, when she was certain he had gone, she swam for shore, dived for her clothes, and retreated into the woods. There, waiting for her, she found a huge terry towel. Julian had brought it from the cottage. His thoughtfulness warmed her heart, and momentarily she forgave him for his mischief.

Dressed at last, she made her way to the cottage.

Julian heard the door open and raised his head to study her. His dark eyes were narrowed and elusive.

"Here, drink this," he ordered. "I couldn't forgive myself if you caught a cold."

"You should have thought of that sooner!" she retorted.

His fingers brushed hers as she took the glass. She reminded herself that she must not show that she was trembling, not because she was cold, but because she was locked away in this secluded cottage with him.

"What harm was done?" he wondered with a dark brow arched upward.

"Men and their egos! You think women are playthings to be toyed with—"

"That's enough, Ann!"

"What else am I to think?

He took a step toward her. With a rough motion he lifted her chin and made her look him square in the eye.

"If I am as bad as you make me out, we wouldn't be here now. We'd be making love, whether you wanted it or not!"

"Brute!"

He laughed. "It would be very easy, you know."

"You would force me!"

"Never," he said with a shake of his head. "I don't force any woman. I never have, I never will. Give me credit for that! The act of love should be wanted and enjoyed by both parties. Equally. Don't you agree?"

He turned away, and she licked her dry lips. The situation was out of hand. He had no idea that she *longed* for him to make love to her. Because she loved him so. But she could not permit him to play his fast and loose games with her!

"I'll be going now," she said stiffly.

He slammed his glass down on the bar and turned back.

"Not yet," he said. "You're not getting out of here without even giving me a kiss."

"Julian—for heaven sakes—why do you do this? Why do you persist in—"

There was no time for any more words. He had reached her, his arms had gone around her with possessiveness, and she was crushed against him, held so tightly that she felt every muscle and bone of him. For a long moment he held her like that, his hands caressing her shoulders, moving along to the small of her back. She had never known such ecstasy. But she could never let him know that. Once again she was aroused to the point where she nearly went limp in his arms. Expertly, gently, eagerly, he began to kiss her, parting her lips, exploring her mouth with his tongue, all the while his hands touched with knowing skill, until she ached with tormenting desire.

"Oh, don't Julian, don't—"

His lips bruised hers one last time, and then with a laugh he pushed her away. His eyes mocked her, and his face was set in a harsh mask, almost as if he hated her.

"So, you don't want me?"

She gasped. He had simply chosen to prove his male dominance over her. Without a second thought her hand came out and slashed across his face, leaving a small, red welt across his cheek. Then she ran from the cottage and climbed into the van. She drove away recklessly, her one thought to escape from him as soon as she could. Hot tears streaked down her face. She felt like a fool; insulted, belittled, ravaged. She had never been so hurt and bewildered. Just when she was beginning to let herself believe the warmth of his kisses, she had been thrown aside like a rag doll. Oh, she hated him! He knew that he could turn her to butter whenever he chose. Probably he was laughing inwardly all the while!

She reached the inn in record time. David was in the pool. He saw her and swam toward her.

"Hi! Are you in a hurry? I'd like to stay a few minutes longer. You were a long time. Anything wrong?"

"No," she quickly lied. "Julian came over to the cottage, and I—I discussed the interior decorating with him. It seems he values my opinion."

"Smart man!" David laughed. "I had a lovely dinner with Mrs. St. Johns."

With that he pushed off and swam toward the other end of the pool. Ann paced about nervously, wishing he would hurry, for Julian might return any minute. She couldn't bear another encounter with him tonight. Or perhaps ever!

David was just getting out when she heard Julian's steps. He paused beside them, giving Ann barely a glance.

"How's it going, David?"

"Great pool, Julian. Thanks for letting me use it."

"Anytime. You like this night swimming?"

"I like swimming anytime," David replied. "It has always been one of my favorite sports."

Julian's black gaze swept toward Ann. "Your sister's very good at night swimming, too."

With that he walked away, leaving Ann standing with a flushed and angry face.

David peered at her curiously. "What was all that about?"

"Nothing," she said sharply. "If you're ready, let's go home. It's been a very long day."

"Sure," David nodded. "I guess you don't want to talk about it, do you?"

"No!"

David grinned. "Okay."

Leaving David behind the desk the next morning, Ann walked toward the office, bracing herself, teeth clenching, fists knotted. *How would Julian treat her?* she thought. *With that smug mockery of his, or with kindness, or even regret?*

She found out in the next few minutes. His hard stride alerted her. He stormed into the room, barely spoke to her, and kicked the door shut with a healthy slam. The black mood lasted all day. He spoke coldly to her, dwelt on the work at hand, and never once let his gaze rest on her for more than a second. With cold, trembling hands she took dictation and typed the letters. She manned the phone and in general tried to be an efficient and impersonal secretary, relieved she still had the job.

She made a couple of attempts to talk to him about Mrs. St. Johns's idea of having a craft show at the inn, but everytime she tried to speak of it, Julian cut her short.

Matters got worse when the old dowager made a sudden appearance, looking daggers at Ann.

"I've had no response to my idea! I really think I've been treated shabbily. I must speak to Julian—"

Julian heard her voice and came to his doorway. "Is something wrong, Mrs. St. Johns?"

"Plenty!" she said, storming inside and closing the door behind her.

She was in with Julian but a few minutes when she came out with a smile of satisfaction on her face.

"Sorry, Ann, I didn't mean to be so cranky just now. I didn't realize you'd had no opportunity to talk to him about it—"

She walked away, humming to herself. Ann had barely heaved a sigh of relief when Julian was shouting angrily at her.

"Why in heaven's name didn't you tell me about the art show? You know that she has her own way around here. How could you let an important thing like that slide?"

Ann gritted her teeth. "You haven't given me a chance. I did try—twice—to bring up the subject, and you snapped me off—"

Julian glowered at her. "Never mind. Just do whatever she wants to further the project." With that he motioned her away.

The tension between them went on for several days. Gradually things eased. Julian spoke more civilly, even smiled occasionally, and Ann began to feel more comfortable in his presence. He didn't touch her again. The businessman had surfaced again. If she took care never to be with him after hours, it would probably be all right. When she looked at his black head bent over his desk, she knew that the old stirrings of love were there as strong as ever. But it could never be. The one man in the world she wanted could never be hers. Yet she had to spend nearly every day with him; hear his voice, listen to his steps in the hall, feel his male magnetism! How could she ever manage to do it?

Chapter Six

Somehow, someway, Ann *did* manage it, even though it took its toll of her nerves. Her pride drove her to be one of the best secretaries Julian had ever had. She worked hard and diligently.

It was about a week after their last visit to the cottage when the phone rang on Ann's desk. She snatched it up.

"Hey, Ann, could you watch the desk for me a couple of minutes?" David asked. "I've an errand to run."

"Be right there."

She had filled in for him on occasion before, and Julian had never found fault with the arrangement.

Viewed from the desk, the lobby had a plush, comfortable look. Julian had done very well with this place. Perhaps he didn't know how to put things together, but obviously his interior decorator had. Yet, it reflected Julian's personality, too. It was vibrant, alive, and yet comfortable. There was an air of elegance, quiet, good taste and a feeling of warmth.

She heard the door open and the sound of a male voice. A guest was arriving. The man's luggage was being brought in. Ann saw it was expensive and had many travel stickers pasted to the sides of it. Then she saw the tall, good-looking man and her eyes widened.

He strode toward the desk and barely glanced at her as he pulled the registration card toward him to sign his name. She stood back, amused, waiting for him to recognize her. She reached up into the little bin for his key and laid it down in front of him.

"Please have them send dinner to my room tonight," he said. "And I'd like the New York paper in the morning. Are there any car rentals nearby? I'd like a sports car brought around tomorrow morning about nine. Anything decent—"

"Of course. Anything you say, sir."

He looked up, startled, recognizing her voice. "Ann? Ann Milan? What on earth—"

She smiled at his astonishment.

"Hello, Tim. It's nice to see you again."

"I don't understand—is this some kind of gag? Did you know I was coming?"

"No. I didn't. David didn't tell me you had a reservation."

"David?" he asked with a frown. "Is he here, too?"

"We both work here, Tim. It's a long story.

You've been away in Europe for several months—
you must not have heard about—"

She broke off. A frown marred his handsome
blond looks. "I had heard, but I didn't realize you
worked here."

"I'm the owner's secretary. David is running the
desk during the daytime hours—"

Tim Bradford was shaking his head with disbelief.
"Well, Ann Milan! Step out from behind the desk so
I can really greet you!"

With a laugh Tim pulled her into his arms and
hugged her, kissing her quickly.

"It's great to see you again, Ann. You know, I've
never forgotten that one wild summer romance we
had."

"Oh, how well *I* remember," she laughed.

"This is going to work out really well," he said. "I
haven't stayed at Terrace Inn since that summer, and
I'm out of touch with everyone. We'll have a lot of
catching up to do."

Just about then, Ann realized that Julian was
standing nearby, that he had overheard and seen all.
A black scowl flashed across his face.

When Tim leaned toward her again, she laughed,
lifting her lips for another kiss. When she looked
again, Julian had disappeared.

Tim insisted that Ann have dinner with him that
night.

"I'm not settled yet, and as you know, I've no car.
Would you mind terribly if we had dinner right here
at the inn?"

"Of course not. In fact, I highly recommend this
place!"

Tim's blue eyes smiled at her. "I think you have a great deal to tell me, Ann. But I know one thing—despite the circumstances, you haven't changed. You're still a knockout—"

"And you still have the kiss of the blarney," she laughed.

"Tonight. Eight?"

"Yes. I'll meet you here in the lobby."

He kissed her cheek and signaled to the boy to bring his luggage. Ann remembered Tim Bradford with mixed feelings. It had been a delightful summer when they had been a twosome. She had been young and naïve. Tim was worldly, handsome, rich. He knew all the right people, said all the right things, went all the right places. She had adored him. But it was a summer thing, quickly forgotten once the cold winds of winter had blown in.

David returned to the desk, and she told him that Tim had arrived.

"You didn't tell me he had a reservation!"

David grinned. "I thought it would be a nice surprise. Someone from better days—how was he?"

"Older," she sighed. "Like me. But still the same Tim. . . ."

She hurried away to finish the work on her desk. Her phone was ringing, and when she picked it up, she was startled to hear Julian's voice.

"Come to my apartment, please. I've some letters I want you to get in the mail."

"Of course. Shall I bring my notebook?"

"Naturally!"

She had not been in Julian's apartment since she

first became his secretary. She wasted no time. Outside his door a few moments later, she knocked lightly. It came open almost at once. She knew instantly that he was expecting a woman. An ice bucket was in evidence and a bottle of wine was chilling. A plate of fruit and cheese was laid out, and music was on the stereo. Her pain was swift and deep. How foolish to be jealous! This arrogant man was not worth her time. If only she could convince herself of that!

"I didn't know you were so well acquainted with Mr. Bradford."

"We're old friends."

He lifted a brow at that and seemed about to say more, but thought better of it. She kept wondering what female had been lured here to the lion's den. Shelley? Probably. Or some other unsuspecting guest.

"You wanted to dictate some letters?" she asked with a cool professional tone.

"Just two. Quick notes."

But before he could begin dictating, his expected guest arrived.

"Ah, Shelley! Glad you could come. Ann, we'll let the letters wait until tomorrow—"

Ann gave an icy smile, nodded politely to Shelley, and whisked out of the room.

"Now, what on earth is so urgent, darling?" Shelley was saying as the door closed between them.

Ann marched back to her desk and slammed her pad and pencil down. She had a hunch that the whole thing about dictation had been staged. He wanted to flaunt Shelley in her face. Because Tim Bradford had kissed her? But Julian *couldn't* care. Not really. She was only a game with him.

She would concentrate instead on her evening ahead with Tim. It would be fun to have dinner with him and be caught up in the old world again. Tim could be charming company, and even though their brief love affair had died completely, they were still friends.

She drove home to change. She dressed with as much flair as possible. There were so few good things in her closet these days. But she had learned to do much with little. Perhaps Tim wouldn't really notice the camouflage. Still Tim always noticed everything.

She reached the lobby a fashionable ten minutes late. Tim had just come down from his room, and he strode across the lobby toward her, wearing a white dinner jacket, his face deeply tanned, his smile as sparkling as ever.

"Ah, Ann! You're as lovely as any woman—anywhere!"

"Tim, you are certainly good for a girl's ego!"

"Come. Our table is ready and waiting. Once we've eaten, I want to take a walk down to the lake, and you can tell me what's been happening."

Over the best wine in the house and during an elaborate and tasty dinner, they talked about old friends and past good times.

"How did you hear about Dad—all the trouble we had?" Ann asked.

Tim slowly put his wine glass aside, and he gave her a brief smile. "Tina."

"Tina Phillips! My oldest and dearest friend? You saw her in Europe?"

"Yes, I saw quite a lot of her. She worries about you, you know."

"Tina's the only friend out of the lot that stuck by me. She's a great gal, Tim."

He nodded. "Yes, she is."

"Why have you come back to the states? I can imagine you much prefer taking Europe by storm."

A grin went across his handsome face. "Business. A matter my father wanted me to handle. It won't take long, so when it's taken care of, I plan to stay on here awhile. I always liked Vermont and the inn. Now that I know *you're* here—"

She laughed. "Ah, Tim, it's good to see you, even when I can't believe half the things you say and none that you imply."

"Silly goose, of course you can!"

He lifted her hand and left a kiss in the palm and folded her fingers over it. "Keep that one. It will grow—later—" he said with twinkling eyes.

"You must have done that very same thing to every attractive and eligible woman in Europe."

He lifted his shoulders in a casual shrug.

"Tell me, where did you run into Tina?" she asked.

"Switzerland," he said. "As usual she was the life of the party."

"Never a dull moment with Tina," Ann replied.

She felt a whisper of melancholy. Once she would have been a part of that happy crowd, without a care in the world except where the next party would be and where the next interesting man might be found.

Tim had guessed her thoughts. "It's a rotten shame, what happened to your father. I always liked him. But bad luck comes to us all at one time or another, I suppose. Worst of all was the accident—and David—I must make it a point to look him up tomorrow. How is he bearing up?"

"David is going to be okay," she said testily.

"Hey, take it easy," Tim said. "It's just that I truly care."

"Sorry. I suppose I am touchy where David's concerned."

They lingered for awhile over their after-dinner liqueurs, then left the dining room to step out onto the terrace where white wrought iron tables and chairs had been placed in a casual manner. Here people were enjoying the night and sipping cocktails. Just beyond that, the pool shimmered blue and clear under the floodlights.

Tim led the way down the path, following the wooden railings, helping her with the last few steps. The path was well trodden and beaten down. Water lapped the shore nearby. Soon they had stepped away from the sound of music and voices. Tim paused. His cigarette lighter snapped on and off, and she saw his tanned, handsome face in the flame. His eyes were shadowed, distant.

"My word, Tim, what *is* it?"

"Jet lag," he confessed. "The time changes really catch up to me after awhile. Do you mind making it a short evening?"

"Of course not."

They returned to the inn, skirting the pool which was busy tonight for the day had been hotter than usual. Ann tried not to think about swimming nude in the lake at the cottage or what had happened afterward.

Tim walked with her out to the van, kissed her cheek a bit indifferently, and called good night. As she drove away, it occurred to her that he had not really told her anything. Something was troubling him.

David was carving half-heartedly on a new piece when Ann reached home and went inside. She was tempted then to tell him of Mrs. St. Johns's plans for an art show, but held back. It would spoil half the elderly woman's fun if she didn't get to surprise him with the news.

"Ann, I've been thinking," David said anxiously. "Maybe I should try and go to business school."

"What about this?" she asked, picking up his half-finished carving and studying it, enjoying the detail, ever amazed at how skillful he was.

"It's a plaything," he said irritably. "Something to pass my time. I'll never be anything but a whittler, Ann."

"Tut, tut," she laughed. "Don't put yourself down so. And you should be thinking about branching out into something really special. These small pieces are nice, but why don't you make something huge for a change?"

He grinned at that. "Ann, you always manage to pick up my spirits. Thanks."

We all need someone, she told herself.

She needed Julian. No one else. Seeing Tim tonight, she had realized that all the more. Tim was fun, she could enjoy his company, but she knew that they would never be more than friends. There was only one Julian Terrace, and even in his blackest moods, she found him intriguing, beguiling, her man.

The next day Julian's mood was more mellow than usual. He seemed restless, decided against dictating the letters that seemed so important last night, and finally called her in with a proposal.

"It's been more than a week since we were over at the cottage. Let's drive over and check the progress. If those workmen haven't made some real strides—"

"You don't need me," she said quickly, coolly. "I've already given you my ideas about the place—"

"I want you to come," he insisted. "Listen, Ann, we've been at each other's throats for days. I'm weary of it, aren't you?"

He gave her that lopsided smile that always yanked at her heartstrings. She knew that, like a reckless idiot, she was letting him work his magic on her again.

"Well, if you insist," she said.

"I do! Let's be on our way."

The drive around the lake was cordial enough. Julian even made an effort at small talk. When they neared the cottage, there wasn't a truck or car within sight. No work was being done today, and Julian swore under his breath. They went inside, and Ann could see the patio door had been installed and the redwood deck had been started. Fresh paint had been applied in the bedroom and the old carpeting had been removed. The bath, however, was still as forlorn and hopeless as ever.

"Plumbers!" Julian said angrily. "It's always the plumbers that hold up everything!"

"Actually, I think there's been a great deal accomplished in a short time."

"I suppose I *am* impatient. Let's go for a swim," he said. "The water looks so inviting."

She flushed from the tips of her toes to the top of her head. Oh, how well she remembered the last time she'd been in the water. She woke up at nights, drenched with the memory of it, hating Julian one moment, loving him the next.

"Oh, not like that, Ann," he said smoothly. "There are several swimsuits here. One of them should fit you perfectly. Just a second—"

He was in and out of the room in a flash, returning with a black one-piece affair.

"Who belongs to this? Shelley?" she said tartly.

His mouth made a straight hard line and his eyes flashed.

"What does it matter?" he asked. "You can use the bedroom. I'll change out here—"

She told herself she should make an excuse and not go. But the water was tempting. It would be fun to go swimming with Julian. Besides, she had herself under control now. She wouldn't let anything foolish happen. And how often did she get to spend time like this with the man she loved?

Her arguments went back and forth. All the while she was pulling on the suit. It was a perfect fit. She went out to find Julian. He was in a pair of blue swim

113

trunks and looked magnificently male. His chest was wide and tanned with a mat of black hair. She remembered the touch of it against her fingers the night she had slept in his arms.

He had a perfect build, narrow hips, long, lean suntanned legs. She tore her glance away, but he was intent on gazing at her. His glance swept her from head to toe.

"Beautiful," he murmured. "Absolutely lovely."

He held the door for her and she walked past him, brushing against him, acutely conscious of his nearness. She breathed the fresh air deeply, trying to bring her reeling senses under control.

They went down the path together, Julian leading the way. He helped her out to the wooden dock built over the water. A small boat was anchored there.

"The best swimming is just up the lake. We'll take the boat."

He helped her in, his fingers cool and impersonal. She perched on the narrow wooden seat, and soon he was pulling the rope. The motor sputtered, fired and began to roar with energy. He handled the boat superbly with the skill of a man who loved being outdoors.

He turned away from the shore, putting the boat quickly through its paces, going so fast that Ann clutched the seat for dear life. If he was trying to frighten her, he was succeeding. He cut a figure eight that sent them rocking back and forth, the wake shaking the boat dangerously.

After a few minutes of this, he eased the motor down and they proceeded more calmly to their destination. Soon he was swinging back toward shore. Only a few boats were out on the lake today, and those were to the far side. "The fishing's best over there," he explained. "But just ahead is the place for swimming. The bottom of the lake slopes gradually, there's shallow water, but there's nice deep stuff, too—and you like to dive—"

He anchored the boat under the hanging branches of a willow tree. The swimming spot was snuggled into the bend of the lake, roofed by overhanging trees. There was a tiny beach of brown sand, just large enough for two people to stretch out on beach towels.

He paused for a moment, his glance meaningful. They were alone! So totally alone, shut off from the world. The nerves tightened in her throat as his gaze held her prisoner.

"Give me your hand, Ann," he said. "Be careful getting out of the boat—"

The boat bounced up and down, unsteady beneath her. She weaved a little, nearly losing her balance. Julian was already ashore. He reached out his long arms to steady her. In a moment, he had swept her up and bodily lifted her out to the safety of solid ground.

"Put me down," she said in a smothered voice.

"In a moment."

He walked with her into the cool shade beneath the trees. There he swung her gently, holding her tighter, his eyes a brown, liquid warmth that seemed to consume her.

"Alone again," he said.

"To go swimming," she reminded him tartly.

She struggled to be free of his arms, and after a moment he let her go, laughing quietly.

"So we will."

He tossed their towels beneath the spreading branch of a huge pine tree and produced a tube of suntan lotion.

"Would you?" he asked.

He turned his back to her and she spread the lotion over his broad shoulders, trembling as she touched him. She loved his smooth, tanned skin. There was one tiny scar, moon-shaped, that she traced with her fingertip.

"What happened here?"

He laughed. "I wrecked my bike as a kid; cracked some ribs, cut a gash in my back. I also nearly broke my nose."

"So you were an arrogant kind of brat."

"I was mad about something," he shrugged. "I lost my head. I don't even remember what about now. You're surely full of questions."

"It occurs to me that I don't know much about you—except what gossips say—"

He motioned for her to continue spreading the lotion.

"What *do* they say?"

"You're very rich. You've been in several kinds of business. That you were a genius to get the old inn going again—"

He didn't deny any of it. As she soothed the lotion over his hard, firm muscles he sighed.

"Ah, that feels good, Ann."

"You're very brown."

"I often go swimming," he said.

"Have you brought Shelley here?"

He scowled and took the lotion out of her hand. "You're obsessed with Shelley!"

"Not me. *You!*" she flared. "Swimming doesn't seem Shelley's cup of tea."

"Is it yours?" he queried. There was a double meaning to the question, as he gave her a rakish grin.

"I'm going in—"

He stopped her with a hand on her shoulder. "Better use some lotion. The sun is very warm, and it's deceptive here. You might get a painful burn—"

"I'll be all right!"

"All the same—I'd rather be sure."

His fingers spread the lotion gently, rubbing it across her flesh in a tantalizing, caressing way. He insisted on covering her back and shoulders, then continued on to coat her thighs and legs. Then, reaching up, he spread lotion across the hollow of her throat. Tenderly, he smoothed the liquid along the top of her breasts at the line of her suit. Sweet ecstasy shot through her like wildfire. His eyes held her gaze and she saw the passion there, a tender ardor she wanted to trust but couldn't.

"That's enough," she said.

"All right," he laughed, putting the cap on the lotion. "We'll go in!"

He snatched her hand and tugged her to her feet. With laughter they splashed into the water. It felt deliciously cool, and when they had waded out far enough, they began to swim. Julian's strokes were long and sure. He was much more expert than she'd expected. He swam lazily beside her, his wet black hair sleek as a seal's. They swam together for several minutes before he nodded to the shore.

"Race you back," he said.

He moved ahead, but by the time they reached the beach, she was only a stroke behind him. He held out his hand and they waded out together.

"I should have been polite and let you win," he said.

"No."

"You like to be competitive?"

"Yes, and I like to win—fair and square."

He spread out the beach towels and tossed her a small one. She dried herself and sat down beside him. He toweled his hair, and she laughed to see it standing up in little wet unruly points.

"What's so funny?" he asked.

She reached into her purse and got her comb. She began to comb it in place, and as she finished, he buried his face against her. "Ah, Ann—this was a wonderful idea."

"Julian, you mustn't—"

"You're delectable."

"Julian—"

"You enjoy this as much as I. Why else would you kiss me as you do? Come, Ann, don't be pious, don't tell me that you want me to stop."

His lips were cool against her flesh, pressing to the hollow of her throat. She found herself touching his head, holding him there, her pulse pounding beneath his kiss.

He moved down slightly, pressing his lips to her

damp shoulders, then to the cleavage between her breasts, and with a gasp she felt his fingers tugging at the shoulder strap, trying to ease it down, to expose a breast to his ardent kisses.

She stopped him.

"No. I can't let you, Julian. It has to mean something, and I know it doesn't. You don't care for me. You run off to see your ex-wife and you're always with Shelley and—"

"Scores and scores of other women," he said with an air of bitterness. "Come on, Ann, don't spoil this moment—"

"Do you woo all your secretaries like this?"

He straightened, instantly annoyed. "You know I don't. I fired the last two—or was it three? Since you came, I have a hard time even remembering the others."

"You didn't tell me when you hired me that there would be extra-curricular activities!"

It struck him as funny. He began to laugh, his shoulders heaving with mirth.

"Ah, Ann, you're priceless! Tell me, do you charge overtime for moments like these?"

"I'm considering it," she said, nodding her head, eyes twinkling.

The warm air was drying his hair now. She rifled her fingers through it and watched it curl and fall into a deep wave. In a moment he had shifted his body, and she found him stretched out with his head in her lap. She peered down at his thick dark lashes, the hard bones of his jaw, the firm lips that she had come to know so well. If a hundred different men kissed her when she was blindfolded, she would know his mouth. She traced the shape of it with her finger.

"I'll pay double time, triple time!" he murmured.

"I'm not for sale, Julian."

He sobered at that. "The man who has you, Ann, would be a millionaire! You're so beautiful—"

"I don't hold a candle to Shelley. Is your ex-wife as lovely?"

He scowled, his mouth tightening in anger.

"Damn it! You can't let it alone, can you?"

"I don't know what you expect of me!"

He was coldly furious. *"Think of us. Now. This minute.* Forget everything and everyone else. Why can't you do that?"

"I'm a realist."

He raised his head and faced her. His fingers gripped her shoulders and she tried to wrench free, but he would not let her go.

"I'm tired of this foolishness. Tired of battling you all the time. It's time I taught you a lesson, Ann Milan. A lesson of love—"

He forced her to lie back. As he leaned over her his eyes were blazing. His lips crushed down on hers. Involuntarily her arms went around his neck, pulling him closer.

"Yes, yes," he murmured. "Ann, darling—"

He pressed harder against her and heaven exploded around her like a million stars. She was seconds away from surrendering when they heard an amused twitter of laughter. Julian's caressing hands stopped and he lifted his head. In a moment he had rolled away from her.

At the same time Julian saw the boat, she saw it, too. It was only a short distance off shore. Two teenage boys were in it, giggling.

"I could break their necks!" Julian muttered.

"They have binoculars on us! How long have they been watching?" Ann gasped.

Julian looked disconcerted. "Hard to say. I guess they hoped they were going to get an education." He was on his feet now, folding his beach towel. "Ann, I think we'd better get back to the inn."

"I'm sure of it!" she replied.

The moment was shattered. She felt unfulfilled and somehow empty. The moment should never have happened in the first place. She didn't want a casual affair. She was too much in love with him for that.

By the time he had helped her into the boat, she had worked up her anger. How could she let herself become involved with such a man? How could she *ever* trust him?

Julian was quiet all the way back to the cottage. Once there he reanchored the boat, and they went up the path. At an outside shower they washed off the lake water and went inside to dress.

On the drive back to the inn Julian said very little. He had turned his mind to the work at the cottage.

"I want you to keep a close eye on it, Ann. Keep me posted on the progress."

He was testy again; his voice hard and impatient. Julian had turned back to the boss. The man who held her and kissed her so ardently had stayed behind at the lake.

When they reached Terrace Inn, Julian paused for a moment behind the wheel.

"Ann—"

"Yes?"

"You're not sorry for today, are you?"

"I don't think it should *ever* happen again."

He lifted his lips in a wry smile. "Spoken like the haughty Miss Milan."

She pushed open the door. "Who now works for you. I have letters to get in the mail—"

She rushed away and plodded steadily at her desk for the rest of the day. Julian stayed clear of the office, and she was glad. It was with extreme effort that she managed to concentrate. Only a short time ago she had lain in his arms—

I won't think of it, she thought, her face feeling hot. *I cannot and I will* not *think of it!*

Julian came to his desk shortly before it was time for her to leave for the day. He wouldn't look at her. In a moment Shelley appeared. Apparently the meeting had been prearranged, for she walked straight into his office, unannounced. Dressed to the hilt, in a hurry. If Julian Terrace couldn't seduce one woman, then he would seduce another! Ann felt used, soiled.

Julian met Shelley in the doorway, reaching out his long arm to pull her inside. The door closed behind them.

Ann slammed her desk drawer shut, snatched up her purse and got out as swiftly as she could.

Give up, she told herself. *Forget him. Let Shelley or his ex-wife have him. Good riddance!*

If only she could find a way to really mean all those ugly thoughts. If only she could stop loving him. . . .

Chapter Seven

Ann decided she would simply concentrate on someone else. Perhaps, if she got lucky, she could stop loving Julian so much. Fortunately Tim Bradford was still at the inn. His business often took longer than he had expected, but they found time for a quick swim or a leisurely dinner. Ann knew that Julian very often saw them together and she flaunted it before him. *How did he like it? It was nothing for him to leave in the middle of the afternoon with Shelley on his arm!* If this was some kind of war, she had no idea who was winning. *And what did he really care anyway?* she asked herself.

The inn was busy. It kept Ann hopping to keep up. Mrs. St. Johns suffered a bout of illness and plans for the art show had to be shelved momentarily. The news of such a project had never leaked out. David still did not know. Mrs. St. Johns had impressed upon Ann that she wanted to be the one to tell him.

Once again, Julian was absent for several days. He didn't tell Ann where he was going, but she could guess. It irritated her even further.

When he came home, ten days later, he was in a foul mood. Apparently it was difficult to tear himself out of his ex-wife's loving arms!

Ann was glad to be so busy with the season in full swing. She and David often had to stay extra hours, and when they were finally allowed a full weekend off, they were relieved.

"Being a working man really takes the starch out of me," David confessed.

"I've a million things to do," Ann replied. "The house is a wreck. I must give it a thorough cleaning, and I have some shopping to do."

"It will be nice to stay at home for a couple of days," David sighed. "Will Tim be coming by?"

"Perhaps. But he's very busy."

The day at home went swiftly and Ann felt she had accomplished something. David grew tired of his carving and fell asleep over a book. When someone knocked at the door, Ann expected to find Tim.

She was stunned to look through the screen door and see Julian dressed in a pale summer suit. He looked so handsome that despite her vow to drop him from her life, she felt a surge in her heart.

"Hello, Ann," he said, eyeing her carefully, studying her reaction to his appearance. "Listen, I know it's your day off—"

"I suppose something is wrong at the inn," she said stiffly.

He tried a smile on her. "No. But it's a mad house. I had to get out of there or go crazy. Let's have dinner somewhere else. If David doesn't mind—"

David looked up sleepily and shook his head. "Matter of fact, Ann's been stirring up such a storm around here, I'd welcome the peace and quiet."

"Don't I have anything to say about this?" Ann asked with exasperation in her voice.

"Nope," Julian said, giving her that disarming grin she could never resist. "You're overruled. Hurry and change—"

"I haven't said I'd go—"

He stepped into the room and she fell back. She hated it that her heart was suddenly unruly, her pulse dancing.

"Just dinner," he said quietly. "Can't we be civil over a little food and wine?"

She weakened, just as she feared she would.

"Oh, all right—"

She could sense he was smiling, pleased, as she hurried away. In a moment she heard him talking to David about baseball and soccer.

She hated to be rushed, but tonight she didn't really mind. In a few minutes she had changed into a white dress accented with touches of blue on the cap sleeves and at the V-line of her throat. Her hair fell to her shoulders in a sunlit shimmer. Excitement brought the silver to her eyes, and when she dashed away to join Julian, her step was lively and quick.

Julian got to his feet, eyes shining with approval. David gave her a saucy wink. Then Julian held the door and they stepped out into the night together.

The sky was crowded with stars. The air was cool, but Julian opened the sun roof on his car.

"Do you mind?"

"No. The air is invigorating. I love it."

They zoomed along into the night. She wondered where he was taking her. But it didn't matter where they went. She was just happy being with him.

Julian seemed determined to put her at ease and talked mostly about business.

"Tomorrow I'd like you to go over and check the cottage," Julian said. "I haven't had any updated report in some time."

"All right."

"Then, too, I want it decided about the art show. If there's to be one, I want it in the next week or so. The sooner the better."

Julian was driving steadily, his tanned hands handling the wheel with skill. They took the corners swiftly, but the sports car was glued to the road. He kept talking about immaterial things. He seemed anxious to avoid any kind of quarrel. Could it be they would have one entire evening together without fighting?

He eased up on the accelerator. Ahead Ann saw a nightclub, neon sign dancing. It was an out-of-the-way-place, new and reported to be a bit disreputable.

"Why here?" she asked.

"Why not? Does it bother you?"

"Not if it doesn't bother you."

"If we're seen, it will be a foregone conclusion that we're having a clandestine affair," he said with amusement.

With that he took her arm and they went inside. They were given a tiny table in a corner. Over candlelight Julian met her eyes.

"I wanted to come here because we're not likely to see anyone we know. There will be no interruptions; we can enjoy our food, talk, listen to the music, dance—and later—"

"Later?" she asked, a catch in her voice.

"I plan to make ardent love to you."

She shrank back away from him. "It always comes back to this, doesn't it?"

"I like what happens between us, Ann."

"Oh, am I so different from other women? Different than Shelley or your ex-wife?"

His jaw set, a muscle twitched in his cheek. "There you go again! Do you ever let up?"

"Do you ever give me reason to?" she shot back.

"I very often see you with Tim Bradford!"

"He's an old friend!"

"Shelley is also an old friend!" he retorted.

They were glaring hotly at each other across the table. Then with a short laugh Julian relaxed and leaned away from her.

"Call it a draw?" he asked.

"Touché," she sighed. Soon she was laughing, too.

"Hmm, that's better," he said. "I love to hear you laugh, Ann. You light up like a warm fire on a winter's night."

"You can be very charming, Julian."

"Listen, tonight let's live for the hour. We won't look at beginnings or endings. Just now, this second—"

"You can also be very persuasive."

He leaned toward her. Lightly he brushed his lips against hers. "Sealed with a kiss," he said, obviously pleased.

The waitress appeared and Julian ordered drinks. When they came he lifted his glass in a toast. "To you, Ann. To tonight. To us."

"May I make a toast, too?"

"Of course," he said.

She met his dark eyes and shook her head. "Nothing. I changed my mind."

"Why? Tell me what you wanted to say?"

"I—I can't."

It had burned like fire in her throat. Just three words. I love you! But she could not say them to this man. Because she could not let him know how deeply she cared. He thought of her as pleasant chemistry, an attraction. He had never mentioned love.

The food was excellent. She was acutely aware of Julian across the table from her; his dark thick hair, his smoldering eyes, his long jaw, and firm mouth.

The music was not as good as that at Terrace Inn, but it didn't matter to Ann. Julian held her close as they circled the floor and she clung to him, wanting him never to let her go.

It was late when they finally left the nightclub. A gentle breeze stirred the tree tops and the stars were still there. Before they had reached the car, Julian had stopped her and pulled her into his arms. His kiss was long and deep, and then they walked on, arms around each other. In the car Julian tuned the radio to some soft music and drove with the windows down. The hills wound away beneath them. They sped along like two free spirits, no care in the world.

As they neared Darshire, Julian pulled the car to the side of the road. He shut off the motor and turned to her.

"I don't want to take you home, Ann. Why don't we drive over to the cottage? See what's been going on there."

"Julian, I know what you have in mind and—"

"Afraid?" he asked quietly.

In the stillness of the car she could hear her heart thundering like wild drums. He was so close. His hand came out and touched her cheek. His thumb brushed across her mouth.

"Don't be," he murmured.

He crushed her to him so hard she gasped. His mouth found hers and he began kissing her ardently.

She broke away, breathless. "Don't. Please, Julian—"

He leaned away, his physical presence still so near that she felt encompassed by it, smothered, buried in it.

"Kiss me, please," he said calmly.

"What?"

"I always do the kissing. Just once I would like for you to kiss me."

She had to laugh. "You're crazy!"

"I'm serious. And I'm waiting, my love. Kiss me."

He was sitting very still. She shook her head with

bewilderment. This man always surprised her. Then carefully, gently, as if in slow motion, she leaned over and found his lips with hers. She explored them as if she had never touched them before and she left a trail of kisses across his mouth and up the side of his face to his eyes. She felt bristly eyebrows, a bony forehead, thick, silky hair, and then she kissed his closed eyes, his long lashes, and the tip of his nose. He was laughing now.

"Honey, you do that awfully well. Nobody ever kissed my nose before!"

"It's a nice nose. Romanish—"

"Hmm. From some long ago ancestor perhaps."

"But you know what I like best?"

"Tell me," he whispered.

"This—"

And her lips came down squarely on his mouth, and with a little groan he pulled her closer and began answering her kiss.

Suddenly there was a light flashed inside the car and they pulled apart guiltily.

"*Now* what?" Julian said.

"Sorry, folks. Didn't you see that sign? No parking here," the state trooper said grinning. "Have to ask you to move on or give you a ticket—"

Julian nodded. "We're going, officer."

Julian started the car and soon they had driven away. Ann began to laugh and Julian was roaring, too.

"I felt like a high school kid parked up on Prospect Hill. They always chased parked cars out of there—" Ann said.

Julian shook his head. "What a way to end my kiss! Not at all what I had in mind. Let's go to the cottage. No one will bother us there."

"No."

"I don't want to take you home," he insisted.

"But you will," she said.

He gave up with a heavy sigh. "Someday, Ann, *I'm warning you,* I'll not take no for an answer!"

"I've told you often enough. I'm not that kind of woman! I don't want to be just a little trinket hanging from your watch fob."

"You're the most infuriating, mistrusting woman I ever met!"

"With reason," she answered, her own anger heating up.

Oh, why did it have to come to this? Why must she always be reminded of the kind of man he was. He wanted only one thing—and it was *not* love!

He pressed down the accelerator, driving swiftly down the road. He wasted no time in getting her home. She climbed out of the car before he could come and open the door for her. The house was dark. David had already gone to bed.

"Good night!" she said acidly.

He didn't reply. His answer was in the furious spinning of the wheels and the roar of the powerful motor. In a moment the sight and sound of him was completely gone. With a sigh she let herself into the house. David called to her from his room.

"Tim wants you to phone him."

"Now?" she asked. "It's late."

"He said it was important."

"All right."

She called the inn and asked them to connect her with Tim's room. The phone rang several times. There was no answer. Either he was dead asleep or he'd gone out.

She got ready for bed and tried to call Tim one last time. There was still no reply and there was no message for her. She hung up with a frown. It worried her. Tim was not the sort that called at late hours.

She had barely put her head to the pillow when the phone rang. Thinking it was Tim, she rushed out to answer it.

"Hello, Tim! Is that you?"

There was a long silence on the other end of the line.

"No, it's not!"

The line went dead and she held the phone for a long moment. It had been Julian! Perhaps just to say good night, perhaps to say more. Now he thought that Tim—

Dear heaven, she thought. *He'll never believe me if I tell him the truth.*

She hung up the phone thoughtfully. The gods were always working against them, it seemed. Even state troopers interfered and came along at precisely the wrong moment.

No, she corrected herself, it was the *right* moment! She could not become any further involved with Julian Terrace, a man who still flew off to see his ex-wife and lolled around the swimming pool with Shelley Dickson! She must *not* let her love grow. She must stop thinking of him. She must never let him invade her dreams again—

The next morning at Terrace Inn she was startled to learn that Tim had unexpectedly checked out last night. A note had been left for her. She read it with amazed eyes.

"What's wrong?" David asked.

"Tim! Tim and my old friend, Tina Phillips. Can you beat that? Why didn't he tell me?"

David made a face. "Tell you *what?*"

She laughed. "Why, they're perfect for each other!"

David shook his head. "Sis, you're not making any sense!"

"They're getting married. He came here to think it over, to get his father's view, and suddenly decided he couldn't stand being away from her. He flew back to Europe to catch up with her—"

David grinned. "Sort of romantic, wouldn't you say?"

"Yes," she said with an audible sigh.

David covered her hand with his and gave her a long, loving look from his brown eyes. "Julian will come around, Ann."

She flushed. "Whatever gave you the idea I cared about Julian Terrace?"

David smiled. "It's written all over you. And if he's got a brain in his head, he won't let you get away—"

Mrs. St. Johns was bearing down on them.

"Hello, David," she said sweetly, then turned her

commanding eyes to Ann. "I have to speak with you, dear. Could we use your office?"

Ann gave David a helpless shrug that made him laugh and they hurried away. Mrs. St. Johns had fully recovered from her bout of illness and had clearly become a bundle of charged energy.

"I had plenty of time to make plans, lying around feeling poorly," she said. "I really want to get this art show underway."

"Julian would like it next week, if possible—"

"Next week!" she gasped. "There's no way we can move that fast. But I'll get started immediately. I want a meeting with Julian. Set it up for me. Perhaps dinner tonight. In my suite. You come, too, Ann. Bring your notebook—"

Ann stared into her closet, despair filling her heart. So many of her nice things were gone now. And old Mrs. St. Johns had eyes like an eagle. She would know instantly that any of her good things were last year's styles. But there was always the good little basic black number, cut in a low V in the front and back. She would add a few pieces of tasteful jewelry (practically all she had now) and perhaps get by.

David gave her the wolf whistle when he saw her. She laughed. "Do you think your old dear will approve?"

David grinned. "Sure she will. What's this all about?"

She laughed. "You'll know soon."

When Ann returned to the inn and knocked at

Mrs. St. Johns's door, she found Julian already there. His gaze swept over her, dark eyes glittering. How handsome he was in his dinner jacket. But Shelley was like an ornament, hanging to his arm, finding excuses to touch him and be near him.

The meeting went slowly over dinner and Ann couldn't wait for it to end. Julian's attentions to Shelley sickened her. He seemed to do it defiantly as if he wanted to show her that he intended to do as he very well pleased. How could it be that in the shadowy night, parked alongside the road in his car, he could be so warm and ardent, and so cold now? Because she wouldn't give in, wouldn't become just another conquest in his long chain of victories?

Her cheeks stung whenever she saw him lean toward Shelley to whisper something in her ear.

Mrs. St. Johns was interrupted by a phone call. The conversation droned on and on. Julian stepped out to the balcony, a cocktail in his hand. In a moment Shelley found an excuse to join him. After awhile she drifted back into the room, looking smug.

"Julian needs more ice in his drink," she said.

Mrs. St. Johns hung up at last. Shelley and Julian returned from the balcony. Ann bit her lip with hot, jealous anger. Shelley's lipstick had left a smudge on his mouth. Ann gripped her pencil so hard it nearly snapped in two.

They talked for ages, and Julian gave in to most of the old dowager's demands. He warned her they would have to be careful about the space they used.

"Dear, of course we will!" Mrs. St. Johns laughed. "We won't clutter too much, I promise."

But Ann knew, as did Julian, that if she decided to take *all* the space, she would.

The meeting would surely never end! Ann's head was throbbing. Shelley was becoming bolder and bolder, and Julian was absorbing her attentions like a sponge. In passing he mentioned his cottage.

"Cottage!" Shelley said, brightening considerably. "You promised to show it to me, remember—"

"When it is all redecorated," he said smoothly. "I want to check on the workmen's progress tonight."

"Oh, let me come with you," Shelley said. "Would it be all right, Mrs. St. Johns?"

The old lady shrugged. "Don't be long."

Julian nodded, said a quick good night, and opened the door. Shelley had gone to get her purse. How smug and confident he looked! Last night he had tried to lure her to the cottage and she wouldn't go. But Shelley was wild to go with him! The thought of the romantic interlude they'd have there sickened Ann.

"Have a very nice time at the cottage!" she said in a scathing voice.

"Wait just a minute!" Julian said, catching her arm with a restraining hand. "You're coming with us!"

"No, I'm not. Three's a crowd."

Anger flashed in his dark eyes but was soon replaced by a look of amusement. "I can't be rude to a guest," he pointed out.

"Of course not!" she said crisply.

With that she walked away swiftly, reaching the elevator before Shelley had appeared in the doorway with Julian. She jabbed the button with an angry gesture.

Sleep would not come. Ann tossed and turned as she thought about Julian with Shelley at the cottage. Perhaps he had even taken her for a night swim at the cove—in the very same swimsuit he had loaned her.

Oh, how could she have gotten so involved with him? In the darkness of her room, with the breeze stirring the curtains she knew that she would have loved Julian Terrace no matter what. From that moment he had kissed her at the Autumn Ball, she had loved him. She, sophisticated Ann Milan, who could have nearly any man she chose, had fallen for an innkeeper, a rogue, a man who shattered hearts and thought nothing of it.

Something rattled against the screen at her window. She sat up with a sense of alarm. Then there was another sound—pebbles perhaps—bouncing off the screen wire. She went to the window and peered out cautiously.

"Ann—" came a low call. "Ann—please—come out—"

"Julian?" She leaned into the window with surprise. "What on earth do you want at this hour?"

He lifted an object in his hand. The light reflected against it enough for her to see that it was a bottle.

"Wine," he called. "Red wine—and two glasses—"

He fished in his pocket and produced them. "The best the inn has. Come on, Ann—come out—"

"No."

"I want to talk to you."

"Tomorrow."

"Tonight!"

"Are you drunk?"

"Sober as a judge," he said. "And I can't go to bed with this riff between us—"

"We've nothing to talk about!" she insisted.

"We've everything to talk about," he replied. "Ann, if you don't come out, I'll come in."

He made a motion toward the window. "I've never broken into any house before, but I will now."

"All right!" she said, believing he meant it. "All right! Give me a moment to get a robe."

She felt her heart thudding in the darkened room. She groped for her negligee and her mules. Then, running a brush quickly through her hair, she left the room.

She let herself out through the front door and across the old porch. There Julian waited, the bottle perched on the step. He had already poured the wine.

"Sit down, darling. Here—taste. The best I could find in a hurry."

The wine was warm, a little tart. Why was he here? What did he want? Heaven forbid, had Shelley left him wanting? She couldn't believe that!

With a laugh he raised his glass. "To the most boring evening of my life," he said. "Until now—"

"Oh, come," she said. "You've never found Shelley boring before, and with the cottage such a romantic setting—"

He was smiling at her. "We never got there."

She sat up straighter. "Oh, Shelley had other ideas—"

"She wanted to see one of the nightclubs in Darshire. It seems Mrs. St. Johns keeps the lid on pretty tight. So I took pity on her and we went to the club—"

"Ah, how sweet!" Ann said icily. "And you danced cheek to cheek and kissed in the candlelight—"

He drained his glass quickly and set it down with a thump.

"It's not what you think, Ann!" he said with a brusque tone in his voice. "You always make it worse than it is."

"But I saw evidence on your face earlier when you were out on the balcony."

He hunched his big shoulders toward her, laughing. She found no humor in it. She would never understand men like him! They thought it fair to play fast and loose with any woman they wanted!

"Shelley kissed me—I didn't kiss her."

"You take me for a fool? I really think I'd better go in now. Thanks for the wine."

"Sit down, Ann," he said firmly. She knew from the rigid set of his shoulders and the tone of his voice that it would be foolish to do otherwise.

He poured another glass of wine, but she had drunk very little of hers. Her head began to ache. He put his hand on her knee and with a fingertip traced the length of her bare leg.

"Lace and satin. Blue?"

"Green."

"Were you asleep? Were you dreaming of me?"

"No!"

He laughed softly. His hand came up now to her hair and caressed it, pushing it back from her face, and in a moment he had leaned toward her. He buried his face against her hair and then reached out to take the glass from her hand. He set the bottle of wine aside and proceeded to pull her close into his arms.

"I'd rather sit on a porch step and watch the stars anytime with you, Ann, than go out with Shelley."

"I don't believe it!"

"Then it's time I convinced you, isn't it?"

He began kissing her, and with each kiss she felt her control slipping little by little. Soon she was holding him close, enjoying his broad shoulders, the firm muscles of his arms, the touch of his hands that could be so surprisingly gentle. At last she pulled out of his arms.

"I must go in."

"No," he said. "A walk. We both need to get some air—"

He tugged her down the steps and they began to walk around the house. The yard was not large, but there were a few rose bushes and a wooden glider left there from the previous owner. They swung there, back and forth, companionably silent. Ann dropped her head to his shoulder.

"Do you realize the summer is getting away?" he asked. "Have you noticed the sun is not so warm in the mornings?"

"Hmm."

"The autumn season will be upon us before we know it."

"And we'll be busy, busy, busy. But it will put money in the till."

"You're catching on fast," he laughed.

"The art show will be over, the leaves will turn, and you'll close the shutters to the inn—then what will you do?"

"Ann, if you're trying deliberately to get me off on the subject of the inn—it won't work."

She laughed. "Won't it?"

"No," he whispered.

He stopped and drew her close to kiss her full on the lips, then he kissed her throat, the soft hollow above the ribbon tie on her negligee. Her skin quivered with the warmth of his kisses.

It was then she heard the phone ringing inside the house.

"David will answer," he muttered.

"No. He's asleep. I'll have to go inside." She tried to pull out of his arms.

"Don't do this to me again, Ann!" he warned angrily. "You drive me to the point of madness and you want to answer a damned phone!"

She broke free and began to run. Gasping for breath, she rushed up the steps to the door. She feared he would never touch her again! She could not expect a man like Julian to keep taking her rejection! But she was surprised to hear him laughing.

"Saved by the bell!" he shouted to her.

She hurried inside. By the time she reached it, the caller had hung up.

Julian had gone. She heard the sound of his car, the soft slap of tires over concrete, as she stood there in the dark. It would always be like this—he would come to her—but he would always leave her.

Chapter Eight

The next day when Ann went to work she found Mrs. St. Johns waiting for her at her desk.

"There you are at last! Come to the dining room with me while I have breakfast. And ask David, too, please. I'll just go ahead—Shelley's waiting for me there, and I have some errands for her to run—"

Mrs. St. Johns had spoken. Ann sighed, but knew that she must jump as commanded. At least David would know about the art show now, and she anticipated his eagerness and enthusiasm.

By the time they reached the dining room, Shelley was finishing her coffee and ready to leave. Ann couldn't have been more relieved. Shelley seemed quiet, perhaps pouting, as she hurried away, scarcely speaking to her.

Mrs. St. Johns gave them her brilliant smile and

insisted they join her in coffee and rolls. "Even if you've already eaten, you must indulge me," she said. "This *is* a very special occasion."

David was still puzzled. He had pounded Ann with questions all the way to the dining room.

"Mrs. St. Johns wants to spring the news," Ann had told him.

"I know something's been going on for days—weeks even. What is it?"

Ann laughed. "She made me promise not to tell you."

Mrs. St. Johns ordered breakfast for herself and coffee for them, all the while watching David covertly, pleased with herself. As they waited for the food, Mrs. St. Johns gave David one of her charming smiles.

"My dear, I've decided to sponsor an art and craft show here at Terrace Inn. I, of course, especially want you to bring a full display of your work."

David stared at her with surprise. "What a great idea, and you know I want to participate!"

She laughed, pleased. "I've wanted to tell you about it, but I wanted to clear away all the obstacles first, just in case something went wrong."

Ann couldn't imagine anything going wrong when the old lady put her mind to it!

"I've arranged for some rather important art critics to visit the showing. Shelley's taking care of some of the details now. Julian has assured me complete cooperation, and of course, I'll be relying greatly on Ann to help smooth out all the rough edges."

"How many pieces should I bring?" David asked, his cheeks flushed with excitement. "And just who are the critics?"

Mrs. St. Johns began ticking them off on her fingers, her diamond rings flashing. They meant little to Ann, for she had never followed the art world very carefully. But David was plainly impressed.

"Garson's judging? My word! I can't believe it. He's a very influential man. He never goes anywhere except to the biggest and most publicized shows!"

"Oh, he's an old friend of mine," Mrs. St. Johns said airily. "I twisted his arm ever so slightly."

Ann hid a smile. She could easily picture her on the phone making demands in her sweet and pleasant way, but beneath it all was always that touch of iron.

"Wouldn't it be great if he liked my work?" David asked. Then he sighed and shook his head. "But I'm an amateur. I know my stuff won't rate a second look."

"Nonsense! You must not think that way, David. I'll expect you to lend us a hand in all of this. I really want it to be successful. In fact, we just might be starting a tradition. If it all goes well and Julian's pleased—who knows?"

Ann was not sure about any of this. For all involved, she hoped it was successful, that it brought business to the inn, and more than anything, she hoped it gave David some real encouragement.

It was the middle of the morning when she finally came face to face with Julian. Somehow they had kept missing each other, either she was at her desk and he was absent from his or vice versa.

"You've been avoiding me," he accused, his dark eyes sweeping over her. "If it's not ringing phones, it's something else."

"I've been pacifying your favorite guest."

He grinned. "Oh. Mrs. St. Johns?"

"Yes. And she's going to liven things up around here with her art show or I miss my guess."

Julian's familiar scowl deepened across his forehead. "Still not sure I like the idea, but then—" he lifted his shoulders in a shrug. "Do you suppose I'm mellowing?"

It was one of Ann's more hectic days. There were more guests now which meant additional work on her desk. Mrs. St. Johns called her about every ten minutes wanting this or that, tossing questions at her that she couldn't always answer. By the middle of the afternoon Ann began to wonder if she could last until five o'clock.

Going out to speak with David, she found him more and more excited about the art show.

"Shelley's been on the phone all day spreading the word. I've handled most of the calls! Several of them to New York, a couple of local newspapers, two more to the local television station—Wow, when Mrs. St. Johns does things, she does them right!"

David's excitement had spread through the inn. It seemed all the employees had caught it.

That evening at home Ann was so tired she was restless. The air seemed stale, oppressive. Perhaps a storm was brewing. She watched David work for awhile, his nimble fingers handling the tools and shaping the wood with skill and eagerness.

But Ann's attention span was short. She paced around outside and finally decided the only way to settle down was to take a drive. There had been no conscious intention of going to Julian's cottage, but soon she found herself turning in that direction. Following the lake road, she reached the drive and pulled the van under the trees. The cottage was dark.

There were all kinds of enticing paths here, and she saw at once that the boat was gone. It was then she spied Julian's car parked to the side of the cottage. Julian had taken the boat and would surely return soon. Her heart began trip hammering, and she told herself that she should leave. But she somehow couldn't make her feet obey the command of her head.

When she heard the boat coming at last, she smiled to herself. She would surprise him.

She was in a rare good mood tonight. Tired though she was, she was eager to see Julian. She ached to be held in his arms again. Perhaps for a little while she could forget her doubts about him.

The boat was easing up to the dock, and soon Julian leaped out to make it fast. Then just as she was about to step out of the shadows and call to him, Ann saw that Shelley was with him. Apparently he was enchanted with her all over again.

Ann's anticipation sank like lead to her shoes. Her cheeks went hot. Of course! How had she persuaded herself to forget what kind of man Julian was? He *had* to have a woman on his arm to feel complete. Casanova! Rake! She despised him!

What shall I do? she wondered.

She didn't want to be seen. She'd never live it down if Julian knew she was here. Creeping away, she hid behind a tree, feeling like an idiot or some bumbling spy.

Julian had his pipe clenched in his teeth. He reached a hand for Shelley and helped her ashore. But in a flash she was off and running.

"Shelley! Wait a minute, will you?" Julian shouted.

"We have nothing more to say to each other. I want to go back to the inn. My dear boss will be wondering where I am anyway. The old biddy never gives me any time to myself!"

"You needn't be so angry, Shelley. Try once in your life to be reasonable!"

Shelley scoffed. "Reasonable! You're insufferable, Julian Terrace. You always have been. I'll never understand what Irene saw in you—"

Julian hurried after Shelley. "That's about enough!"

"Well, it's true! I'm glad you're divorced—glad, do you hear? For Irene's sake—"

Soon they were out of earshot. In a moment Julian's car started up and they drove away. Ann knew she should be glad that they had quarreled. But she knew it wouldn't last. It hadn't before. Tomorrow they would probably be as cozy as ever.

She slumped against the tree feeling absolutely lost. There was no hope. Tears began to trickle down her cheeks. Finally she walked out to the dock and sat there, feet dangling over the water. The air turned suddenly cool. A stronger breeze was stirring the tree tops.

I should go home, she told herself. *There* is *a storm coming.*

But she didn't want to go. Somehow, some way, she had to come to terms with herself, make herself stop loving Julian so much.

But how?

She lingered too long. With a sense of alarm she realized dark clouds had blotted out the stars. Summer was on the wing—autumn was creeping up fast—and it was not unusual for weather patterns to change abruptly at this time of year.

A flash of lightning forked out of the sky. She ran for the van. There was a tremendous cracking, snapping sound just above her head. She screamed.

Flashes of light and balls of fire bounced around her feet. She was terrified. Too late, she realized what the noise meant. The lightning had struck one of the huge pines. It was coming down!

Run! she told herself. *Run fast—*

She sped as quickly as she could. The tree came rumbling down with a terrific roar. One of the branches caught her and knocked her down. She was pinned to the ground.

She was stunned, unconscious for a few minutes. When she opened her eyes, rain was striking her face. She tried to move, but the heavy branch had imprisoned her. She wasn't certain, but she thought nothing was broken. Only bruised. She might lie here helpless all night in the rain. She shivered in fright. But David would miss her. He would phone—alert someone. That could be hours though. Meanwhile, she had to suffer it out, keep her courage, keep her head. Pray.

The storm was becoming worse. She began to feel as if the branch would press the very life out of her. It was pointless, but she began to yell for help. She shouted at the top of her lungs. Soon she would be too hoarse to even whisper.

This must have gone on for more than half an hour. All sense of time was lost. There—had she heard something, a car? Had she seen headlights turn toward the cottage? It was impossible to tell. Her vision of the cottage was blocked by the fallen tree.

"Help!" she shouted again with one last burst of hope. "Somebody, please help me!"

Footsteps! Undeniably, footsteps!

"Where are you?" came a shout.

It was Julian!

"Over here. Julian, over here!"

It took a few minutes for him to find her, even more for him to lift the enormous branch and free her. Then he picked her up in his arms and hurried up the path to the cottage. Somehow he got the door unlocked and the lights turned on, all the while keeping her in his arms.

"Are you hurt?" he asked anxiously. "Any broken bones?"

"Just got the good sense knocked out of me, that's all."

He laughed with relief. "Thank goodness for that! I'll get you some brandy. You're drenched."

"So are you."

"We could undress, towel off," he suggested.

"I'm woozy in the head, but not that woozy," she retorted. "How did you happen to come back?"

He sloshed brandy into a glass and handed it to her. She sipped it, feeling the warm fire spreading down her arms and legs.

"I saw your van as I drove away."

"Lucky for me that you did."

"I was curious as to why you were here."

"Just restless," she said quickly.

He smiled at that and came to refill her brandy glass.

"And you came here?"

She flushed. "It's peaceful here. Tell me, what did Shelley think of the cottage?"

His dark eyes glittered. "She found it attractive."

"And Irene?"

His face went dark and moody.

"Irene never liked it. She loathed it, in fact. She had her own idea of what kind of place she preferred—"

"A villa on the French Riviera, of course!"

His eyes had gone to cold stones.

"She's difficult, demanding, you've no idea—"

Ann didn't believe a word of it. It was just a cover-up. If it were true, would he go jetting off to see her whenever the mood struck him?

"She's impossible, if you must know," he said dully.

Ann's lips curled in disgust. Surely he didn't expect her to swallow that. Not when he must have spent a small fortune setting her up in a swanky villa!

"Just thinking about her gets me so wrought up—"

Suddenly, in a wild burst of temper, he flung his glass against the stone fireplace. Bits of glass went shattering through the air. One of them deflected and bounced back to leave a small gash in his forehead.

Ann gasped at the sight of blood. "You've hurt yourself!"

She ran to get a wet cloth. He stood dumbly, staring at the mess he'd made.

"Sit down, Julian," she said. "Let me tend to this."

He sat obediently, woodenly, as if he only half-heard or understood. Gently she dabbed the cut, stopping the bleeding.

"I hope there's no glass in there. Maybe tomorrow you should have a doctor check and see."

"Sorry," he muttered. "Sorry—I'm all right, Ann."

She tended to the wound with a touch of pity and sympathy for him. Why did thinking of Irene upset him so? Could she be wrong about him? Oh, she wanted to be. She longed to be!

When she finished, he lifted his head, and his eyes smiled at her.

"Thank you."

"Does it hurt?"

"Not now," he murmured. "Not since you've touched it."

She wanted to move away from the blaze of his eyes and the warmth in his voice. But she wasn't quick enough. He was on his feet, pulling her to him. His fingers pressed urgently into her flesh. With a reckless fierceness he held her close. His mouth sought hers, on fire with passion, seeking, searching, probing. The world tipped dangerously out of control.

"Please, don't, Julian. Don't play with me. Don't use me!"

"Be quiet," he whispered. "Just be quiet, Ann."

He kept kissing her, exploring her lips, taking from them all the warmth and love she had held in check for so long. His hands caressed her body, molding her to him. She came alive under his touch. Ecstasy moved in with bone-weakening intensity.

Outside the storm was still raging, shutting them away from the world. Rain thundered on the roof, wind howled at the windows.

With one bold motion Julian swept her up into his arms. His eyes were hollow pits of black passion. He moved toward the bedroom and pushed the door open with his knee. His face was a mask of naked desire.

"I saved your neck awhile ago," he said in a low, intense voice. "Now you save mine!"

He put her on the bed, leaning over her with burning eyes. His mouth covered hers with reckless passion, and in one helpless moment of surrender Ann put her arms around him. He pressed his lips to her throat. His hands began caressing her, lifting her up on a wave of desire that threatened to drown her.

The wind suddenly burst open a window and fresh cold air swept into the room. With it Ann's senses came back.

She pushed him away, gently, firmly.

"No, Julian. I'm sorry, no—"

He muttered angrily, but finally moved away from her. He slammed the window shut, and by then Ann had run from the room.

"Ann, Ann!" he shouted. "Come back to me."

She sped from the cottage and stumbled through the rain to the van. Once there she started the motor with a rush and pulled away. She saw him leaning in the doorway, a tall, lean man with rigid shoulders, watching her go. When she was out of sight of the cottage, she stopped the van and lowered her head to the steering wheel. She let the hot tears flow. He would never forgive her. He would grow tired of trying to prove that he wanted her. But desire wasn't love. Not once had he said he loved her—she tried to think all sorts of bitter, angry things about him.

But her heart bled with despair and the sweet, harsh pain of unrequited love.

Chapter Nine

Ann was grateful that for the next few days there was no time to think of anything but the art show. When she saw Julian, he treated her coolly and impersonally. It was as if they were strangers, and Ann found it was better this way, even though seeing his dark, unhappy face tore at her nerves and unsettled her reserve. But she had her own pride which she drew constantly on. Ann Milan had been brought to her knees by her unfortunate circumstances, but no one could take all of her pride away. It was a part of her breeding, a part of her make-up, and she lifted her chin and squared her shoulders and went on with the business of living.

It didn't mean that her heart didn't ache or that there were moments when she thought the facade she'd built around herself wouldn't break into a zillion pieces. It didn't mean that she didn't lie awake at night and think of Julian with such need and intensity that she thought she couldn't bear it. It didn't mean that she would ever forget him or that her love would stop. It wouldn't.

"Ann, you're not paying attention!"

Ann brought her thoughts up short and met Mrs. St. Johns's glaring gaze. "Oh, I'm sorry. There are so many details, and I'm doing my best to keep everything running smoothly. Now what was it you said?"

"I really think this one artist will be crowded in such a small space you've alloted him. Can't we shift that artificial plant over next to the door?"

They'd already had a long and heated discussion about the plant with Julian. He felt as if they were stripping the place down to bare walls and carpet. But as usual, Ann found herself giving in, and after that Mrs. St. Johns was as sweet as sugar.

David was going at such a high pitch, he was blind to Ann's suffering. He talked of nothing but the show. At home he argued with himself as to which pieces to display. He had started a new piece and hoped to finish it in time, laboring far into the night. While Ann tossed and turned, unable to sleep, she would hear the little cutting sounds of his tools biting into the flesh of the wood. Sometimes she would get up to go out and watch.

"I'm keeping you awake!" he said with alarm. "I'm sorry, Ann."

"How's it coming?"

He gave her a fervored look from his blue eyes and a shy grin. "It's my best, Ann. I really think it's the very best I've ever done."

"But it looks—unfinished—"

"It's supposed to," he laughed. "It's a kind of new form I'm experimenting with. Ann, do you think Garson might possibly like it? I mean do you think he'll give my stuff a second look?"

"Of course! I'll dare him not to," she said.

"No—no special favors. I don't want him to know that I'm—well—temporarily disabled. . . ." He paused to pat the wheelchair. "Not that an old hard-head like Garson is apt to do anyone a favor, I still don't want him to know. If I get any recognition out of the show, I want it to come honestly."

"It will. You must be tired. You've been at this for hours."

"I can't afford to be tired. Not now. I have to finish, Ann, and in time."

"How about a break then? A cup of hot chocolate, some toast—"

"Hot chocolate would be good."

"I'll fix it."

She was glad to have something to do to keep busy. She fixed the hot chocolate richer than usual and beat whipped cream into it. David seemed thinner all the time. The work was taking its toll in energy he really couldn't spare. But she wouldn't dream of stopping him. It was something he felt compelled to do and it was wonderful to see him so excited.

She took the hot chocolate back to the living room and insisted he stop for awhile to drink it.

"Okay. Fifteen minutes. Then I'll work until two or two-thirty, then quit for the night."

"Promise?"

"I promise," he nodded. "If you'll promise to go to bed and go to sleep. You've been looking dragged out, Ann. Dark circles under your eyes, and you're jumpy as a cat—"

So he had noticed after all!

"Want to tell me about it? Listen, I know something happened between you and Julian. All anyone has to do is look at either of you."

"I don't think I can talk about it, David. Not yet. Maybe some day—"

"If he's hurt you—if he's done anything—" David knotted his fists ready to defend her. She leaned over and put a kiss across his white knuckles. "Relax, dear brother, your valor is not needed. I can handle Julian Terrace."

He sighed at that. "I'm not so sure."

"Well, I am."

He changed the conversation to the art show. He was itching to get back to work, so she left him there, the adjustable table pulled up close over the arms of his wheelchair, the block of wood coming under the fine touch of his carving tools. Head bent, he was lost into another world. Ann called good night, but he never heard her. She fell asleep at last to the constant thud of chisel and hammer and David's contented grunts of satisfaction.

The art show crept ever closer. Posters advertising the event had been placed all around the inn and in many shops and stores in Darshire. It was mentioned in the paper, touted on the television and spread by word-of-mouth. The interest was high. Artists began to emerge, eager to show their crafts. Much native and local work would be on display; everything from dried apple dolls in various costumes, to oil paintings, to David's wood sculpture.

Mrs. St. Johns began to put the work into classifications. Ribbons and awards would be made for the winner in each class.

Julian stomped through the lobby to look at the progress, murmured something under his breath, and went on. His glance slid toward Ann, but quickly moved away. He had not looked directly into her eyes since the night at the cottage. He seldom called her into his office, but wrote his letters in long hand and left them on her desk for her to find in the morning. Ann saw with a twist of heart that he and Shelley had mended all differences and were apparently thick as thieves again.

People from New York began to check in. Garson was one of the first.

"He's here!" David said with awe. "Garson's really here. I can't believe it!"

"He's only a man," Ann cautioned.

"Try telling him that!" David said with an uneasy grin.

Garson was tall and thin with a white clipped mustache and the coldest blue eyes Ann had ever seen. He talked of New York, of the artists he knew, kissed Mrs. St. Johns's withered cheek graciously and made them all laugh with a wry kind of wit. But it was not the kind of humor that put Ann at ease. She feared the man and hated his power.

The day of the show at last! Ann and David reached the inn early, and together they set up

David's pieces. He had chosen to display them on swaths of velvet, choosing exactly the right color for each carving. These were placed on small pedestals and tables. Ann suggested a floodlight, but he shook his head. "No, the natural light would be best. The floodlight would make it too artificial. I think this is best."

Other artists, more than a dozen of them, came early as well. Soon the lobby was filled with all sorts of paintings, sculpture, and native crafts. One old woman was displaying a set of china, hand painted, delicate and unique. Ann was fascinated by it, but more by the artist herself, a woman from the back woods with rough hands, a mail-order dress and heavy shoes.

The show was to begin officially at ten o'clock. Julian had been persuaded to have his chef provide hors d'oeuvres and fruit punch. Before ten the people were coming. Ann saw David tense as they stopped to look at his work, but he stayed behind the desk, officially on duty.

The demands on Ann were limitless. Mrs. St. Johns was summoning her constantly to do this or that. The art show went along smoothly. There was a lull in the morning and once again in the afternoon, but Ann was truly surprised by the people who came.

The crucial moment came about three o'clock when Garson strolled in, carrying a cane and smoking a cigarette in a long holder. He looked at each piece of art carefully. When he reached David's, Ann found herself clutching her hands tightly. Behind the desk David had gone tense and white!

"Relax," she whispered to him.

"How can I?"

When Garson had seen everything there, he disappeared with Mrs. St. Johns. David gave Ann a nervous smile.

"What do you think, Ann?"

"Impossible to tell."

But she feared that Garson had not been impressed. It seemed to her that he had passed over David's work rather quickly. For the next thirty minutes Ann paced restlessly, trying to be cheerful to guests while waiting for Garson to return. Mrs. St. Johns had been given the honor of bestowing the ribbons and awards to those Garson had judged the best.

In David's category it was soon apparent that he had not won. The first award went to the man from New York, the second to a local woman. David's eyes went blank. She saw him slump in his chair and turn his head away.

Ann's heart bled for him. She bit her lip so hard that she cut it with her teeth. Julian suddenly was beside David, hand clamped on his shoulder in comradely despair.

"Should have known," David said thickly. "I should have known!"

"There will be other art shows, other chances," Julian told him.

David didn't reply. He turned away in his wheelchair and maneuvered through the crowd and outside. Ann started after him, but Julian stopped her.

"Let him be alone for a little while," he said.

"Yes," she nodded. "I suppose that's best. Oh, I wish we'd never had the show! I wish—"

"You can't always protect him."

"Ann—"

She found an apologetic Mrs. St. Johns standing before her. She was near tears, too. "I'm so sorry for David. Garson simply passed him over. I really thought—"

"I wish you'd never encouraged him!"

Mrs. St. Johns stiffened with indignation. "My dear, one showing does not make an artist! Remember that. David still has a tremendous future ahead of him. Unless he lets this one little failure get the best of him."

By now Ann had lifted her chin and got hold of herself again. "David's no quitter, Mrs. St. Johns."

The old lady smiled. "Good! I'm glad to hear it. Where is he? I'd like to speak with him now."

"He went outside for a moment."

Mrs. St. Johns moved away. Ann longed for five o'clock when everyone would take their art objects and clear out of the lobby. With David away from the desk she had to cover for him. When she saw Garson standing before her, she braced herself.

"Yes, Mr. Garson, may I help you?" she asked impersonally polite.

"Oh, Miss Milan. Yes, you can. I'd like to check out now. I'm due back in New York for another show tomorrow afternoon."

She took care of the details while Garson waited impatiently.

"By the way, there was a sculptor's work on

display here today—same last name as yours. Any relation?"

Ann met his cold blue eyes with equal coolness. "My brother. Ordinarily he runs this desk."

"Oh?" he said with surprise. "The man in the wheelchair?"

Ann gave him a piercing look. "Temporarily in the wheelchair," she amended. "And he does have other attributes."

"Of course. Sorry. He shows great promise, you know. Too bad there isn't an award or a ribbon for that."

Ann stared at him. "Do you mean that?"

"My dear," he said icily superior. "Garson never says what he doesn't mean. Where is the young man?"

"Licking his wounds. Outside somewhere."

With that he moved away, and Ann held her breath. If he would somehow convince David that there was truly something special about what he was doing!

The press of business kept Ann from seeing David until it was time to go home. She and Mrs. St. Johns had overseen the taking down of the displays. There were hands to shake and conversations to make.

All the way home David looked straight ahead and Ann's worries increased. Nervously she waited for the dam to burst. But she waited all through their simple dinner. Afterward, instead of carving, David settled down with a book.

"David—"

"I'm all right, Ann!" he said quickly. "I just don't want to talk about it right now. Okay?"

"Sure."

But his aloofness was hard to deal with and she didn't know what to do about it. It lasted for several days. He was quiet, pleasant, spoke when spoken to, but ventured little on his own. When she talked to Mrs. St. Johns about it, she was met with a rather casual attitude.

"Oh, give him time, Ann. He'll be all right." Mrs. St. Johns gave her a smile, but said nothing more about David. "I'm not going to stay as long as usual this year," she said. "In fact, in a couple of weeks I'll be leaving. You might want to advise Julian."

"Why go so soon? You'll miss the peak of the autumn color!"

"Affairs take me away. I'm going to Europe from here."

"I see."

But she didn't see at all. Somehow while Mrs. St. Johns was around, she felt there was a future for David. It was possible that her enthusiasm for her brother had waned. Poor David!

Julian was nearly as aloof as David, becoming more moody, almost boorish. Except where Shelley was concerned. Then it seemed he turned on all the charm he had.

He seemed to be avoiding Ann. It was just as well. There was no future with him, but it did nothing for her bleeding heart.

Then one afternoon he called her into his office.

"I have just spoken with the carpenters in charge of the work at the cottage. There have been all kinds of senseless delays. I want to go over there and check it out once again. Come along."

"I have considerable work on my desk. Things got behind during the art show—"

"Stop it, woman! Didn't you hear me? You're to come along."

"Is that an order?" she asked with a lifted chin.

"What do you think it is?" he asked.

There was nothing she could do but agree to accompany him.

Autumn was in the air. Touches of color were already coming to the trees. The air was spiced with wood smoke. Spider-web clouds drifted through the sky. When they turned toward the lake, she saw it shining back at the sun, twinkling and blue.

Without realizing it, she sighed.

"It *is* a very special place," Julian murmured softly.

They had scarcely spoken all the way, and now he turned to her with eyes that were surprisingly kind and gentle.

His gentleness turned to anger once they had reached the cottage.

"It will *never* be ready in time!" he burst out furiously. "What is the delay this time, I wonder?"

"You have a specific completion date in mind?" she asked.

"Of course! As soon as the inn closes for the season, I plan to move in here."

"I see!"

But she didn't at all. He had stayed at the inn last winter. Did this mean someone was going to share the place with him?

He sensed her thoughts.

"This happens to be very important, Ann."

"I'm sure it is," she said coldly. "When will *she* arrive?"

His black eyes glittered dangerously. She watched his dark brows make a straight line. The corners of his firm mouth lifted up sardonically.

"You never give up, do you?"

"How can I? You're the kind of man who has to have a woman in the picture."

"The only woman I want in my picture is you, Ann Milan."

She swallowed at the sudden dryness in her throat. Oh, if only she could believe that! But how could she? She stared at him, watching his dark eyes glow with a kind of tenderness that set her heart hammering.

"I'm going to convince you, Ann, if it's the last thing I do. But not now, not here. Tonight over dinner. I'll tell you a good many things, my love."

She tried to shake her head, to protest, but he laughed and reached out to stroke her cheek with his long, cool fingers.

"You can't deny me one evening, Ann," he said.

She weakened far too easily and quickly. "All right. One evening."

"Eight o'clock. No, seven," Julian said. "I've waited long enough."

She shivered under the intensity of his words and nodded. "I'll be ready, Julian."

His eyes were glowing with golden lights as they went back to the car, carefully not touching, but devouring each other with their gaze. Ann's heart had started singing. Some last resistance had given away. Tonight—tonight—something truly wonderful awaited them.

She felt on the brink of discovery. She could almost sense the words of love on his lips, the words she wanted to hear above all others. She began to tremble in anticipation.

Chapter Ten

Problems at the inn snapped Ann back to the world of reality. There was trouble in the kitchen. She had two letters to type and get in the five o'clock mail. It was hard to push back her dreams and anticipation for their evening together.

Then Julian's phone rang. It was an overseas call, and he took it with a frown, slamming his door shut. Ann's lips tightened. Was Irene calling again? Would he go running off to be with her?

Suddenly his door came open and Julian looked pale and drawn. His glance passed over her almost blindly as if not seeing her.

"Julian, what is it? What's wrong?"

"I don't want to see anyone. Do not disturb me."

"But, tonight—"

"Off," he said. "Keep everyone away. Do you understand?"

Only hours ago he had held her in his arms and filled her with sweet anticipation. Tonight was to be a night of sweet promise, and now, suddenly without explanation, it was off!

A lump came to her throat. She struggled with her work through blurry eyes. Her hands were shaking and cold. Five minutes later she heard Julian speaking over the phone, and in another five, Shelley appeared.

She made straight for Julian's door.

"I'm sorry, Shelley, he doesn't want to be disturbed."

Shelley looked through her and went on in. It was Shelley he had just called! Ann caught a glimpse of her moving into Julian's waiting arms.

In all that had happened to her in the past few months, all the hurts, the slights, the miseries, *this* was the worst. How cruel could he be? He had brought her to the brink of surrender, only to thrust her aside for another woman. Shelley had won after all!

She couldn't sit there another moment. It was nearly five o'clock anyway. She collected David and drove home. He seemed preoccupied. In fact, he didn't notice how she gripped the wheel so tightly or how her eyes had gone hollow with pain. Julian was lost to her. Forever, it seemed. It was all she could do to hold back the tears.

Once they were inside, David hobbled over on his crutches and collapsed in the easy chair.

"Ann, I have to talk to you. I don't think this is a very good time, but I can't put it off. I have to tell you now."

She felt her nerves tense even tighter. Somehow she felt she was on the brink of still another deep canyon.

"What on earth is it, David?"

"A couple of things. They both came at the same time and I wanted to think about them."

She went to sit down close beside him.

"Garson talked to me the day of the art show. He liked my work. It was good, he said, but not good enough to compete with some of the older, more experienced artists that day. But he thinks I show promise. He wants me to study in Europe. There's a well-known sculptor there who will take on promising students. He has offered to help me get into the class."

"Europe! Oh, David, that sounds exciting! You have to go!"

He swallowed hard. "I told him it was out of the question."

She stared at him. "But why?"

"It takes money, Ann."

"We'll get it! Somehow, David, you must have this chance!"

"I couldn't ask you to do this."

"I *want* to do it!"

David reached out and took her hand for a minute, gripping it tightly. "I know you mean well. But this is something I have to do all on my own—if I do it at all. I—I have to, Ann. I can't go on leaning on you forever."

"David, I *want* you to go!"

He nodded slowly. "But you see what I'm trying to say?"

"Yes," she said, feeling sad.

David smiled. "I don't know what I would have done without you, Ann. In those awful days after the accident, you pulled me through. It was you, Ann, nobody else."

She lowered her head. "Oh, if only the accident hadn't happened. If only—"

"Don't look back," he said. "I've learned that, Ann. Don't look back!"

"We have to do something about this, David. There has to be a way."

He smiled. "I told you I had *two* things to talk to you about. Well, this one will probably give you an even bigger jolt."

"I think I can handle it."

"Okay. Mrs. St. Johns has made me a very attractive offer. It seems she and Shelley are not getting along. She's going to let Shelley go, and she has asked me to be her new traveling companion; a sort of secretary. She's promised that we'll tour all of Europe, see all the museums, the famous paintings, the Louvre, the Sistine Chapel—oh, Ann, I *want* to see those places! I *want* to go. She's told me she'll pay me enough so I can make my own way—"

Ann was stunned. Involuntarily, she glanced at the crutches leaning by the chair. "But what about the accid—" she asked before she could stop herself.

David's eyes sparkled. "The doctor says that I have made a remarkable recovery. All that swimming helped." He smiled. "He thinks that I will be walking by midwinter—though of course, with a cane. And, if I do my exercises—Oh, Ann, what do you think?"

"What do I think? Oh, David, you can't say no to any of this! Of course, you must go with her. You can see and learn so much!" She jumped up and hugged him.

"Then it's okay? You'll be all right without me?"

"Oh, David, I'll miss you terribly. But this is your life, your big chance. We can't just let it slip by!"

David squeezed Ann's hand. "Spoken like a true Milan, Sis! I can hardly wait to tell Mrs. St. Johns! She's already made plans to leave early, you know. I'll have to go when she goes—"

The next day, after almost no sleep at all, Ann went to the inn. She had decided that she would never let Julian know how much he had hurt her. She would never give him the satisfaction. Somehow she would get through this day and then the next and the next. She steeled herself for the sight of him. But his office was dark. Only a paper and a pencil lay on top of his desk.

"Ann! Ann!"

David was painstakingly making his way on his crutches towards her.

"What is it?"

He paused beside her desk, hesitated for a moment. "Maybe I shouldn't tell you, but I suppose someone else will. Shelley's gone. Bag and baggage. Early this morning."

"But you expected this, didn't you? You said she and Mrs. St. Johns weren't getting along. You're going to replace her—"

David drew a deep breath. "Julian went with her."

"What!"

"They left—together—the doorman heard them talking—"

Ann struggled to grasp the meaning of all this. "You mean he's run off with Shelley!"

David lifted his shoulders in a shrug. "I think so, Ann."

When David had gone back to his lobby desk, she went into Julian's office. His favorite pipe was gone. The desk had been tidied as if he expected to be away. On a pad of paper she saw he'd been doodling, perhaps while waiting on the phone. His name and Shelley's had been written there, along with a flight number and time. He had called for plane reservations for the two of them!

News of their departure together was a juicy item of gossip all over Terrace Inn. When Ann saw Mrs. St. Johns in the dining room, she nearly asked her what she knew about it, but changed her mind. They were gone—together—what else mattered?

Ann's pain was exquisite. She trembled all over, sickened with the knowledge that she'd been right about him all along. He *was* a philanderer. He had no deep feelings for her. The night that she had anticipated so much had never happened and, at best, had probably just been one of his romantic maneuvers that would have meant nothing!

It was all Ann could do to stay at the inn, to carry on with her duties. But she reminded herself that Ann Milan was made of better stuff than that. She wouldn't turn tail and run. David had made a new life for himself. She would too.

It didn't help matters any when Mrs. St. Johns

phoned and asked her to come to her suite. There she would be reminded of Shelley and, in turn, picture her snug in Julian's arms enjoying his kisses.

Ann knew she owed the old dowager a great deal. She had given David the chance to find himself. She must forget all about Shelley Dickson and think of that.

Mrs. St. Johns answered her knock at once.

"Come in, Ann. Of course you know I want to talk to you about David."

"Your plans for him are wonderful!" Ann responded warmly.

"It will be a treat for me too, you know," said Mrs. St. Johns. "It will be fun to see Europe through fresh, young eyes again. But I wanted to talk to you about it. I know you rely on him very much. I wanted to be sure that I had your consent—that you would not be too lonely without him."

Ann was astonished to see Mrs. St. Johns's eyes soften. Who would have guessed that the stern old dowager had such a warm heart! "Of course I won't," she assured her staunchly. "It's the best thing in the world for David, but are you sure that it won't be a nuisance for you—with his—disability—"

"My dear, I'm a selfish old woman," Mrs. St. Johns said with a twinkle in her eye, "I took the precaution of talking to David's doctor before making the offer. Dr. Lazzare assured me that David would be on his feet within the year. Of course, he will have to be conscientious about his therapy, but I will make sure that he is."

Ann impulsively threw her arms around Mrs. St. Johns's neck. "How can I thank you for what you have done for both of us?" she began, planting a kiss on her carefully rouged cheek.

"You don't have to, child," said Mrs. St. Johns, looking pleased. Did Ann detect moisture in those usually commanding eyes? "But now," Mrs. St. Johns said, in her customary brusque tones, "if you'll excuse me, I have a great deal to do before we leave, especially without Shelley here to help me—"

"Shelley's not here to help you?" Ann echoed stupidly. *She might have known.*

"No. She left unexpectedly. A family crisis of some kind."

A likely excuse, Ann thought.

"Doesn't matter. I can manage somehow without her," Mrs. St. Johns said.

"I'm going to miss you and David," Ann told her.

"Who knows, perhaps you can join us later."

"Who knows?" Ann echoed.

But she frankly didn't know what her future held. She could not stay here and be near Julian. She had managed to save much of the money she'd earned. It would tide her over until she could find other work. But she knew perfectly well that Europe would not be in the offing for her.

Three days later, Julian was back—alone. He looked tired and drawn. He scarcely glanced at Ann as he swept by her desk.

"Come in, please," he said.

She snatched up her notebook and followed him into his office. He sat down with a tired sigh. He looked ghastly. For a moment, he covered his face with his hands. She ached to touch him, but he wasn't hers to touch. She longed to know where he'd been and what had happened.

"Any major problems while I was away?" he asked at last.

"A few. Somehow, among us all, we handled them."

"I'm sorry there wasn't time to explain—"

"There *was* time," she said angrily.

He looked at her for a long moment and then nodded. "I somehow couldn't talk to you about it. I wanted to keep you apart from that side of my life."

"And Shelley? Isn't she with you?"

His dark eyes filled with a kind of sympathy. "She stayed. She'll be coming back to the states a bit later."

"I see. How could you bear to leave her?" she asked coldly.

He stared at her, puzzled. "Ann—"

"Talk about fools! I've been the worst—the absolute worst!"

"Wait a minute. You don't understand—"

"Oh, I understand all right," she said bitterly. "If it wasn't your ex-wife, it was Shelley. It seems between the two of them, you were always very, very busy."

He leaped to his feet, his eyes burning hollowly as he stared at her.

"You really believe—you really think that I was just stringing both of them along—"

Ann lifted her trembling chin. "What else can I think?"

A little muscle began to jump in Julian's jaw. He was angrier than she had ever seen him in all their times together. He leaned on his desk, palms down, hunching toward her.

"There was an accident, near Irene's villa," he said with clenched teeth. "Irene was killed."

Ann gasped. "Oh, dear!"

"Irene was a demanding, difficult woman. She was always hounding me for money, even after our divorce. She plagued me every chance she got. Finally, to get her out of my hair, I set her up in a villa, hoping that would satisfy her. Of course, it didn't," he said with an air of tiredness. "But that doesn't matter now. Shelley has stayed behind to take care of the details—"

"Shelley?" Ann asked. "How does she figure into any of this?"

He gave her a cold, tight smile. "Shelley was Irene's sister. My former sister-in-law. We were old friends—"

"Friends!" she gasped.

"It would appear, Ann, that you thought the worst of me. You truly believed I would make love to you when I was still involved with other women!"

She opened her mouth to speak, but she was so stunned by the turn of events, not a word came out.

He was growing more furious with her by the minute. She had never seen him so enraged.

"You must think me some sort of maniac. All right, think the worst. You will anyway! I don't want to see you again, Ann. I thought you'd changed, but obviously you're still the high and mighty Ann Milan who likes to look down her nose at everyone else!"

He thrust his arm toward the door, livid with anger.

"Go! Go!"

She went, nearly running, closing the door behind her, cheeks aflame. She groaned with the impact of the truth. Now she'd ruined everything! He was so disgusted with her, he would never look at her again.

Ann sunk into her chair with a cry of despair. What did she do now? Should she just pick up her purse and leave? But where should she go, and what would she do? Most of all, she didn't want David to realize there was any kind of problem. If he suspected there was, he would never leave her to go with Mrs. St. Johns.

She did not see Julian the rest of that day. Hiding her turmoil from David, she went to work the next morning as if nothing had happened. But her heart was heavy. She knew that Julian hated her now. She awaited David's departure with mixed emotions. She would sorely miss him, but once he had safely gone, she could take her leave of Julian Terrace and the inn forever.

There was a note on her desk written in Julian's heavy hand.

"Make arrangements for the Autumn Ball."

The blood drained out of her face. It had all started for her at the dance a year ago! Now he had the gall to order her to handle the details, knowing quite well that this must be like salt in a wound. Of course, that *was* it! He was deliberately making her pay, enjoying the idea of the torture it would afford her.

She drew a deep breath. Perhaps she deserved it. She had been so horribly wrong about him. Her head spun in turmoil. She lifted her chin and told herself she would not let this get her down. She couldn't fold up at this stage of the game.

The ball! She had to think about the ball. There would be a great deal of work to handle, and the sooner it was over the better. She gritted her teeth and dug in.

Julian swept into the office without a glance in her direction. He stalked like an angry bull, slamming the door after him. He didn't summon her inside but royally ignored her. Ann's heart thudded with swift, harsh pain.

Somehow, some way, she struggled through each day, keeping busy, avoiding Julian, being coolly polite to him whenever it was absolutely necessary to speak to him. He treated her in the same aloof, indifferent manner. They appeared to be total strangers.

Luckily, Mrs. St. Johns decided to stay long enough to attend the Autumn Ball. Having David near helped Ann keep her chin up. He must never suspect her unhappiness. She was glad that he was so caught up in plans for his new life that he never suspected things were going badly for her.

The night of the ball quickly approached. It was to be a very gala affair. Reservations were coming in thick and fast. There wouldn't be an empty table this year.

Autumn had been brought inside the inn. Bright leaves decorated the tables. The favors were tiny candy pumpkins. The orchestra was one of the best in the area. It looked as if Terrace Inn would close for the season on a very high note.

Ann wished she felt as high. Julian made only one request of her, directly, standing before her desk with hard eyes and a set jaw. He wouldn't take no for an answer.

"You'll be my hostess," he ordered.

"I'm *not* coming to the ball."

"You're coming!" He spoke with his old superior tone, putting her beneath him. His gaze was black and demanding.

"All right! You're still the boss!" she said scathingly.

He was out for revenge. She would be forced to stand beside him and greet the people as they arrived; smile, laugh, be gay! All the while her heart would be breaking. Julian would be that cold, hard-hearted stranger beside her; no longer the gallant, handsome man, who only last year had kissed her so ardently and won her heart forever.

It would be Ann's last night with Julian! David and Mrs. St. Johns would leave tomorrow. With David safely away she would not go to the inn again. She would never stand beside Julian again, nor hear his voice, nor do his bidding.

With a lump in her throat, Ann chose her gown for that night very carefully. She chose blue, for she knew that Julian always liked her in that color. With hair swept up loosely at the nape of her neck, the dress a filmy cloud around her lithe body, she was prepared to face the music.

What a bittersweet time it was!

With her heart leaden and her throat choked with emotion, Ann told David she was ready. He looked happy and relaxed. Driving away in the van, Ann was aware of the cool, crisp night. The chill was deepening, the leaves were falling in the wind. Somewhere a jet airplane streaked across the sky, a far away call that echoed along her bones in a terrible rush of loneliness. She sighed. *How do you stop loving a man?*

"You're awfully quiet," David said.

She flashed him a smile. "Just going over in my head all the last minute things I must check."

"Will you need help?"

"Not tonight," she said. "Your work officially ended at the inn this afternoon. I know Mrs. St. Johns wants you at her table. Have a good time tonight, David."

"I will. She's a doll, isn't she?" he asked happily.

"Yes," Ann sighed. "She really is."

Once they reached the inn, David hobbled away to find his mentor. Ann took a deep breath, wondering how she could ever get through the night.

The music had started, and a few guests had already begun to arrive. Ann reminded herself that she had to play hostess, and she must never let Julian know what a toll it was taking of her heart.

"Ann—"

Julian waited for her. He stood very tall and quiet; a handsome man with burning dark eyes narrowed into golden slits as he appraised her. She saw the graceful way he moved, the thick black hair that she longed to touch. His heavy brows were lifted into a sardonic scowl as she walked toward him. She answered with a haughty lift of her chin.

"Miss Milan, I believe," he said with an arrogant bow.

"Good evening, Mr. Terrace," she replied coldly. "You're late."

She didn't apologize, but swept past him to take her place at the ballroom entrance. In a moment, he joined her.

Never had she been so acutely aware of Julian. How straight he stood; how quick his smile came, how deep his voice rumbled as he greeted guests. His laugh was free and pure. Women ogled him with open invitation in their eyes and clung longer than necessary to his hand. He flirted outrageously, made the men feel comfortable, dispensing charm to everyone. Everyone but *her!*

She loved and hated him all at the same time.

It came time to leave the door and go to their table. Julian held her chair, bending low, brushing his lips across her hair. She froze, but would not look at him. He sat opposite her, studying her with frank interest. His gaze rested for a long time on her swept-up hairdo, then the soft hollow of her throat. She began to tremble inside. How much longer could she sit here like this and endure the nearness of him?

He lifted his glass to her with a mocking smile.

"We've had a memorable summer."

She swallowed hard. What game was he playing now?

"I won't forget it, Ann."

She made herself harden her heart. "I won't remember it!"

He brought his heavy brows together in a quick scowl. His jaw tightened with new fury. All the time they sat opposite each other, she could see that he was growing more angry by the minute. Then the food was gone. There was an announcement, and the spotlight swung to them.

Julian got to his feet, all charm and good looks. He reached a hand to her, putting a bright smile on his face. From between clenched teeth he spoke to her.

"As my hostess we're expected to open the dancing. Come Ann, don't make a scene, or by heaven, I'll turn you over my knee and spank you, in front of everybody!"

All eyes were on them. The spotlight illuminated her every motion and expression. She made herself smile. With cold fingers she reached out to him.

She was in his arms! Unbelievably she felt their hard strength go around her. He whirled her about the floor, dipping and weaving. The spotlight followed them, and she was conscious of her fast breathing and flushed cheeks. Julian's eyes were hard and bright.

At last others began to join them. Finally the spotlight turned away. She heaved a sigh of relief.

"I want to stop now. My duty is done!"

He tightened his arm around her. "Not a chance."

"I want to go home!"

"No way!"

"I'll make a scene!" she threatened.

"I think you would! Well, then, I'll have to take matters into my own hands."

At that, he stopped dancing. His big hand imprisoned hers, and he tugged her along, winding through the crowd. There was no chance to escape him.

The fresh, crisp air rushed against them. They moved quickly away into the darkness. With a gasp Ann saw they were walking the very same way they had walked last year. *Oh, the water over the dam since then,* she thought with an aching heart. She saw with a sense of alarm that he was leading her to the very same tree, the exact same shadows. Music drifted out from the inn. It wove in and out with the thunder of her heart. His hand tightened, and it did no good to try to pull away. He was determined. Finally, under the shelter of the tree where autumn leaves were falling, he spun her around to face him.

With quick, eager fingers his hands were in her hair, pulling out pins and combs, dropping them to the ground. Her hair fell to her shoulders in a soft scent of silkiness.

"You know I like it down," he said. "That's much better."

His hand was on her throat, framing her face, fingers cold and hard against her cheek. He made her look up at him. In the dim light she could tell that fire burned in his eyes.

"Now, come here, Ann!"

He surrounded her with hard, strong arms, pressing her against him. She was acutely aware of his familiar body.

"One kiss, Ann, for old time's sake!"

His mouth bore down, exploding with raw passion. With a moan of ecstasy she gave him back his kiss, clinging to him.

"Just like last year," he said, lifting his head at last. "Only now I find you sweeter, dearer."

"Last year? I didn't suppose you cared or remembered—"

"It began for me then, Ann. I've loved you ever since that night!"

Her head was spinning. "Loved me!"

"I've wanted to tell you so many times. But whenever I thought I could make you believe me, you accused me of being some kind of woman-crazy heel—"

Her head was reeling as she struggled to understand.

"But everytime I saw you, there was a woman on your arm!" she retorted.

He lifted his shoulders in a shrug. "Well, perhaps that's true—"

"It *is* true!" she exclaimed. "You know it's true. What was I to think—how was I to understand—"

"That none of it meant anything?" he asked gently. "All I know is that after I kissed you here that night a year ago, I've wanted no one else. I couldn't *see* anyone else. Only you, darling Ann."

Could she believe? Did she dare open her heart at last to this man she had adored for so long?

He pulled her a little closer. "Darling, it's been hell without you these last days when I thought I'd lost you forever—"

"But you sent me away—"

"In a moment of anger," he said. "I've been such

a fool. Ann, do you believe me when I say I love you?"

Tears were filling her eyes. She pressed her head to his chest and heard his wildly pounding heart.

"Please, say it again."

He laughed and lifted her face. "I'll say it every day of our lives, if you'll marry me."

"Oh, Julian—Julian!"

His mouth found hers again, and the sky exploded with stars. With a gasp of pleasure she moved deeper and deeper against him.

"You didn't answer me," he whispered.

She smiled into the darkness. "Oh, of course, I'll marry you. That way, I'll be certain you're mine, that you'll have no time for any other woman—"

For a moment he was angry until she began to laugh.

"You little minx!" he murmured with delight. "I'm going to have my hands full with you, I see!"

His fingers reached out to stroke her hair, and in the cool autumn night he pledged his love to her.

"For the rest of my life, darling. Would you like to live in the cottage? It's why I was in such a tearing hurry to have it completed. I've planned this for so long—"

"Sure of yourself, weren't you?" she asked with false haughtiness.

He rocked her in his arms and pressed his lips to her forehead.

"Why are we talking so much?" he wondered. "There are far better things to do—"

Then he bent his head and his mouth found hers, willing and eager. They were locked in each other's arms while the autumn wind blew and the leaves drifted gently to the ground.

ROMANCE THE WAY
IT USED TO BE...
AND COULD BE AGAIN

Contemporary romances for today's women.

Each month, six very special love stories will be yours

from SILHOUETTE.

Look for them wherever books are sold

or order now from the coupon below.

$1.50 each

___ # 1 PAYMENT IN FULL Hampson	___ #25 SHADOW OF LOVE Stanford
___ # 2 SHADOW AND SUN Carroll	___ #26 INNOCENT FIRE Hastings
___ # 3 AFFAIRS OF THE HEART Powers	___ #27 THE DAWN STEALS SOFTLY Hampson
___ # 4 STORMY MASQUERADE Hampson	___ #28 MAN OF THE OUTBACK Hampson
___ # 5 PATH OF DESIRE Goforth	___ #29 RAIN LADY Wildman
___ # 6 GOLDEN TIDE Stanford	___ #30 RETURN ENGAGEMENT Dixon
___ # 7 MIDSUMMER BRIDE Lewis	___ #31 TEMPORARY BRIDE Halldorson
___ # 8 CAPTIVE HEART Beckman	___ #32 GOLDEN LASSO Michaels
___ # 9 WHERE MOUNTAINS WAIT Wilson	___ #33 A DIFFERENT DREAM Vitek
___ #10 BRIDGE OF LOVE Caine	___ #34 THE SPANISH HOUSE John
___ #11 AWAKEN THE HEART Vernon	___ #35 STORM'S END Stanford
___ #12 UNREASONABLE SUMMER Browning	___ #36 BRIDAL TRAP McKay
___ #13 PLAYING FOR KEEPS Hastings	___ #37 THE BEACHCOMBER Beckman
___ #14 RED, RED ROSE Oliver	___ #38 TUMBLED WALL Browning
___ #15 SEA GYPSY Michaels	___ #39 PARADISE ISLAND Sinclair
___ #16 SECOND TOMORROW Hampson	___ #40 WHERE EAGLES NEST Hampson
___ #17 TORMENTING FLAME John	___ #41 THE SANDS OF TIME Owen
___ #18 THE LION'S SHADOW Hunter	___ #42 DESIGN FOR LOVE Powers
___ #19 THE HEART NEVER FORGETS Thornton	___ #43 SURRENDER IN PARADISE Robb
___ #20 ISLAND DESTINY Fulford	___ #44 DESERT FIRE Hastings
___ #21 SPRING FIRES Richards	___ #45 TOO SWIFT THE MORNING Carroll
___ #22 MEXICAN NIGHTS Stephens	___ #46 NO TRESPASSING Stanford
___ #23 BEWITCHING GRACE Edwards	___ #47 SHOWERS OF SUNLIGHT Vitek
___ #24 SUMMER STORM Healy	___ #48 A RACE FOR LOVE Wildman

Silhouette Romance

___ #49 DANCER IN THE SHADOWS Wisdom
___ #50 DUSKY ROSE Scott
___ #51 BRIDE OF THE SUN Hunter
___ #52 MAN WITHOUT A HEART Hampson
___ #53 CHANCE TOMORROW Browning
___ #54 LOUISIANA LADY Beckman
___ #55 WINTER'S HEART Ladame
___ #56 RISING STAR Trent
___ #57 TO TRUST TOMORROW John
___ #58 LONG WINTER'S NIGHT Stanford
___ #59 KISSED BY MOONLIGHT Vernon
___ #60 GREEN PARADISE Hill
___ #61 WHISPER MY NAME Michaels
___ #62 STAND-IN BRIDE Halston
___ #63 SNOWFLAKES IN THE SUN Brent
___ #64 SHADOW OF APOLLO Hampson
___ #65 A TOUCH OF MAGIC Hunter
___ #66 PROMISES FROM THE PAST Vitek
___ #67 ISLAND CONQUEST Hastings

___ #68 THE MARRIAGE BARGAIN Scott
___ #69 WEST OF THE MOON St. George
___ #70 MADE FOR EACH OTHER Afton Bonds
___ #71 A SECOND CHANCE ON LOVE Ripy
___ #72 ANGRY LOVER Beckman
___ #73 WREN OF PARADISE Browning
___ #74 WINTER DREAMS Trent
___ #75 DIVIDE THE WIND Carroll
___ #76 BURNING MEMORIES Hardy
___ #77 SECRET MARRIAGE Cork
___ #78 DOUBLE OR NOTHING Oliver
___ #79 TO START AGAIN Halldorson
___ #80 WONDER AND WILD DESIRE Stephens
___ #81 IRISH THOROUGHBRED Roberts
___ #82 THE HOSTAGE BRIDE Dailey
___ #83 LOVE LEGACY Halston
___ #84 VEIL OF GOLD Vitek
___ #85 OUTBACK SUMMER John
___ #86 THE MOTH AND THE FLAME Adams
___ #87 BEYOND TOMORROW Michaels

- -

SILHOUETTE BOOKS, Department SB/1
1230 Avenue of the Americas
New York, NY 10020

Please send me the books I have checked above. I am enclosing
$_____ (please add 50¢ to cover postage and handling. NYS and
NYC residents please add appropriate sales tax). Send check or
money order—no cash or C.O.D.'s please. Allow six weeks for delivery.

NAME_____

ADDRESS_____

CITY_____ STATE/ZIP_____

Silhouette Romance

15-Day Free Trial Offer
6 Silhouette Romances

6 Silhouette Romances, free for 15 days! We'll send you 6 new Silhouette Romances to keep for 15 days, absolutely free! If you decide not to keep them, send them back to us. We'll pay the return postage. You pay nothing.

Free Home Delivery. But if you enjoy them as much as we think you will, keep them by paying us the retail price of just $1.50 each. We'll pay all shipping and handling charges. You'll then automatically become a member of the Silhouette Book Club, and will receive 6 more new Silhouette Romances every month and a bill for $9.00. That's the same price you'd pay in the store, but you get the convenience of home delivery.

Read every book we publish. The Silhouette Book Club is the way to make sure you'll be able to receive every new romance we publish.

READERS' COMMENTS ON SILHOUETTE ROMANCES:

"You give us joy and surprises throughout the books . . . they're the best books I've read."
— J.S.*, Crosby, MN

"Needless to say I am addicted to your books. . . . I love the characters, the settings, the emotions."
— V.D., Plane, TX

"Every one was written with the utmost care. The story of each captures one's interest early in the plot and holds it through until the end."
— P.B., Summersville, WV

"I get so carried away with the books I forget the time."
— L.W., Beltsville, MD

"Silhouette has a great talent for picking winners."
— K.W., Detroit, MI

* names available on request.